# AUTISM FEELS...

## AN EARTHLING'S GUIDE

ORION KELLY

# AUTISM FEELS...

## AN EARTHLING'S GUIDE

DEAN
PUBLISHING

First published in 2023 by Dean Publishing
PO Box 119
Mt. Macedon, Victoria, 3441
Australia
deanpublishing.com

Cataloguing-in-Publication Data
National Library of Australia
Title: Autism Feels... An Earthling's Guide
ISBN: 978-1-925452-61-7

Bionic Reading® was proudly used in some parts of this book.

Bionic Reading AG
Masanserstrasse 194
CH-7000 Chur
Switzerland
info@bionic-reading.com
bionic-reading.com

HEY!

Do you ever wonder why the world is the way it is? I sure do.

Some neurotypical topics make absolutely no sense to me.

Look out for my Random Rants icon where I question everything you thought you knew.

Enormous thanks and eternal love goes to my wife Renee who has done so much for me, you are my calm in the storm.

To my sons, Conan and Hugo, I love you endlessly but let's be honest, you've done bugger all*...

*Australian for "contributed nothing but shortening my life."**

**Autistic for "I love them deeply."

# **CONT**ENTS

# **INTROD**UCTION

Don't take this the wrong way but even though you've taken the time to buy my book, I'm still going to introduce myself. Sure, it may seem a little redundant, but it's my book, not yours. Okay, technically this copy of the book belongs to you but it's still mine in a legal sense... you know what? I don't want to get into a full-on discussion on property law so let's move on.

**Hi, I'm Orion Kelly, that Autistic Guy.**

As anyone who knows me or is a fan of my videos and podcasts will agree, I'm a straight talker. My mind knows no other way but to tell it as I see it. So, let's not pretend this book is something it's not. This is not a textbook about autism and I am not a psychologist, or a doctor. Granted, I was referred to in my childhood by my one-and-only mate as Doctor Hook, but that was in reference to my epic basketball skills.

Anyway, I'm just an Autistic guy trying to emotionally connect with you by sharing my personal, bare, raw, sometimes unbelievable yet brutally honest lived experiences as an Autistic person. Since my diagnosis later in life, I've devoted my time to advocating for the Autistic community through my podcasts, YouTube channel, blogs and speaking engagements.

I'm by no means alone as an Autistic person diagnosed in adulthood, and like the many others I've spoken to, it was a life-changing moment for me. It gave me my freedom. But it also took away the person I thought I was. The person I had built to fit in and make others comfortable. This never worked by the way. My diagnosis gave me the "why" behind so many of the unexplainable, painful, uncomfortable, and profoundly damaging experiences throughout my life.

After a lifetime of Autistic experiences, and the many lessons and emotions uncovered since my diagnosis, I'm now aware of so many things that could have helped me so much over the years! In fact, I am now busting with information to try and reach every person on this planet and increase their level of understanding, appreciation, and *Like my guts after too much dairy.* acceptance of Autistic people. The Autistic community is a wildly misunderstood, under-utilised, uncharted, and underestimated resource to the wider community, the workforce, our families and sometimes even to ourselves!

**The intention of this book is to drag as many
misconceptions about autism out of the
Dark Ages and into the light.**

Every last word is drawn from my own personal, raw, lived experiences of being an Autistic person married to a neurotypical (not Autistic) wife, and being a father to an Autistic son and a neurotypical son in 21$^{st}$ century Australia. All so I can reveal a truer perspective to individuals, families and the wider community, as well as reaching workplaces and all levels of government.

My rock-solid belief is that my uncensored, straightforward insight will help increase understanding while promoting new ways to support Autistic people in every setting: at home, in education and employment, and importantly social and relationships of every kind.

This book seeks to break down barriers and increase the acceptance of not just Autistic people but all neurodivergent peoples, so every individual can live life on their terms; each day living as their authentic selves, reaching towards a quality of life that anyone else born into this world deserves.

I have been strongly driven to share my lived experiences and opinions in an honest, open, and public way due to the lack of understanding, acceptance, appreciation, compassion, and kindness I experienced and witnessed around me for decades.

As a law school dropout, I must stress that this book is my opinion and I don't speak for anyone else.

# EVERY AUTISTIC PERSON IS DIFFERENT

We all have individual challenges and strengths. We all have different, and in my opinion, fluid care and support needs. These are my own lived experiences, thoughts, and opinions. And regardless of what you think of them, please know that my only intention is to make a positive difference to the Autistic community. For me kindness is telling the truth.

If you have listened to my podcasts or watched my YouTube videos, you know I often do this through challenging the status quo (I see issues in their clear-cut form, free of societal and neurotypical thinking) and creating long-overdue discussion on how we can improve the way we see and do things.

And now I have expanded my passion for more open and inquisitive conversations around real Autistic experiences with the creation of this book. This process has been well outside my comfort zone, and it's taken some tough questions and strategies to get the job done. I would describe myself in the writing process as a big old cargo tanker that struggles to get moving and pick up speed, but once it does, look out I'm coming through!

After my family, all my energy goes towards raising the level of understanding, appreciation, and acceptance of the Autistic community; this is my purpose.

I know we can all do and be better:
a better friend, better neighbour,
better parent, better partner, better boss.

And I mean as a whole community we can learn to embrace and support and *applaud* the neurodiversity of individuals in every setting.

Prior to my diagnosis as an adult, I had spent all my life thinking I was a bad person because no one liked me or accepted me as I was, or understood how I acted and interacted. "But how can that be?" I hear you protest. "You have a successful broadcasting career, you're a mildly famous content creator. You communicate all the time!"

But as you'll see, my interest in radio and broadcasting is my passion, my obsession, my fixation. And for Autistic people, our passion is like oxygen; it's our lifeblood, to do what we are obsessed with on a daily basis. For me, I learnt some hacks to help my volume, tone and speed of talking (pretending to talk in slow motion for me equates to a "normal" speech range for neurotypical people.) And I'm often alone on the job while I ask endless questions to satisfy my insatiable curiosity about literally everything. I work behind a one-way safety barrier, a studio, which is really like sitting in a safe, familiar box all day with no surprises; it can't be a more Autistic-friendly job.

I also absolutely love making podcasts and videos to share with people about being Autistic. Which in reality is me, alone in my house talking to myself (and a smartphone) hoping someone will watch it. There's no two-way communication there, no social engagement; I am talking about something that I'm passionate about while sharing my lived experiences, and I could go on for hours, barely pausing for breath.

As for small talk or staying engaged in something I'm not interested in, forget it, no chance. So you can begin to see, socially I have rarely found friends, or been able to keep them. But recognising Autistic traits in myself, and recognition by others is the beginning of a positive new approach to form new relationships, creating common ground to understand one another whether as family members, colleagues, or friends.

But I'm starting to rant now away from my introduction, as I'm wired to do when I get passionate. Back to business. You have picked up this book because you may suspect you or someone in your life is Autistic; or perhaps because you are a parent or carer of a neurodivergent child looking to develop a better understanding and appreciation of them.

You may have a partner who is Autistic and the daily relationship struggles seem to be growing. Maybe you are none of the above and you simply have a desire to learn more about autism and Autistic people. Or, last but not least, you are an Autistic person who wants to feel less alone in this neurotypical world.

In all cases, I also I strongly suspect you feel the urgency that more information needs to be shared with the entire community right now! Following the 2022 Senate Select Committee on Autism report[1] that attempted to objectively evaluate the services, support and life outcomes for Autistic Australians, it certainly succeeded in one thing, highlighting this stark and shocking figure:

**Autistic Australians are likely to die 20 years earlier than the average Australian.**

20 years! This is staggering and unacceptable in modern day Australia! The report also states an Autistic person is eight times more likely to commit (or attempt) suicide and is twice as likely to have a mental illness or comorbidities. Unemployment rates for Autistic people are at 80% and they're unlikely to finish Year 12. I believe this is because conventional education does not meet the needs of Autistic people, and so the unemployment stats are influenced by the school dropout rate; it's a debilitating cycle!

The report shows the National Disability Insurance Scheme in Australia (NDIS) serves more Autistic people than any other group. Despite this, the organisation cannot serve them sufficiently due to "Poor understanding of autism within the community and among service providers."[2]

Imagine a government organisation that is shown not to be able to do its job by a government report! This is mind-blowing and reveals how collective governments have effectively failed the Autistic community over many decades. We see clearly that more needs to be done to improve the opportunities and quality of life for Autistic people – **yesterday!**

Obviously without a time machine (or a pre-constructed wormhole), I have to work with what I've got, which is first-hand knowledge, lived experience and a mission to get this information out to as many people that care right now!

And those who don't – but will.

My bottom line is to get this book into the hands of many to make meaningful and lasting change in Autistic and non-Autistic people's lives.

How this book works is very straightforward. For those who would love to hear about the raw background of my early years heading towards my adult diagnosis, keep reading through Chapter 1. However, if your interests lie elsewhere, jump straight to the part you're desperate to understand more about; for example exploring Autistic traits, anxiety triggers or neurodiverse relationships.

I often use a lot of subheadings. That's because I am good at unravelling the challenges that countless home, social, education and work settings can present to an Autistic mind. The power of breaking them down and describing them in simple terms can't be underestimated. It's often the smallest detail that a neurotypical person would miss, that actually has the potential to deeply affect an Autistic person and their behaviour, to the confusion of others in the same setting.

I will break apart why those settings can be tough and bring new ideas to the table that focus and utilise the strengths of Autistic people, remembering that no two Autistic people are the same, so presenting the right information (or asking the right questions) at the right time for each individual is imperative.

Front loading or signposting a conversation is a game-changer for anyone looking to improve their relationship with an Autistic person. For me, if my wife gives me a heads up about something or what may be asked of me, I can try and prepare accordingly. Little tips like that can make huge changes in any environment and experience.

So let's jump in for an enlightening ride and I guarantee you'll learn a lot, laugh, cry, be surprised and come out with hope for change for you or the Autistic people in your life. No time to lose, let's do this, it's time for the change (and healing) to begin.

Not in a legal sense, just in a you-look-good-in-those-jeans white-lie sense.

## 📢 NEEDLESS TO SAY

Why do people preface an unnecessary statement with the phrase "needless to say"?

Firstly, I'll be the judge of what is and isn't needless to say when it comes to information I'm being told.

And secondly, if you really believe the information is apparent and does not need to be said, why are you saying it?! Needless to say, you're the **village idiot!**

AUTISM FEELS...

# CHAPTER 1 | **BO**RN **AUTI**STIC

M y life is far from ordinary; yet extraordinary is not the word I'm looking for either. I am a proud husband to a uniquely beautiful woman inside and out, and a father to two inspiring and equally annoying young sons.

**I am Orion and I am Auti**stic.

Before you jump to any assumptions (even unintentional) let me point out once again that no two Autistic people are the same. We each have individual challenges, strengths and support needs. Therefore, you cannot know what it means for me to be Autistic unless I spell it out very specifically.

Similarly, I cannot speak on behalf of other Autistic people. Advocating for and speaking on behalf of are two very different things. Not that all allies (neurotypical people that advocate for the Autistic community) understand this, even today.

For me, being Autistic means I am eternally curious about every little detail of a story (I will interrupt you for the contextual detail you have left out—repeatedly if I have to) and I'm a deep overthinker to the point of exhaustion. I have intense focus and fixations.

I don't understand why mates play golf to talk, eat and drink. That's what a café or restaurant is for. Friendships are something I have never been good at. ⟶

*Would you shut up! I'm trying to play golf here!*

I am candid and forthright: I can only speak the truth as I see it. It doesn't occur to me that your default preference is to be lied to and shielded from the truth. Who wants that? My openness and directness have never matched society's rules and expectations, and so I have spent most of my life frustrating, offending or unknowingly pushing people away.

The signs and signals from people's body language and cues from facial expressions elude me. For years I didn't understand why. I just assumed I was a bad, broken person destined to suffer through life.

Since childhood I have wondered, *Why is it wrong to speak the truth in every situation, to point things out to people? Isn't it helpful to spot and convey all errors? Why don't people understand me? Why do they take me the wrong way?* And so, I was eternally frustrated growing up; I couldn't put my finger on why so many interactions ended badly; was it all my fault?

I knew I was different from the kids around me, even my own siblings. I stood out by my behaviour, my sensitivity and reaction to sounds, smells, textures or criticism, my constant questioning, even by the way I talked, the brusque tone, speed or volume I unconsciously used. I love my family, but I have never felt like I belonged, like I was one of them.

The impact of people's negative impressions of and reactions to me growing up had an enormous effect on my sense of belonging, when I was still too young to know who I was or why I was a certain way. I watched the world move to a design that I couldn't understand. The world I saw didn't match how I wanted to *be* in it. The noise, confusion and expectations to do certain things at certain times overwhelmed me. There were rules and regulations when I didn't want them and then none when I did!

I would love to share a rolling film of rose-coloured memories with you, but my relationships and experiences growing up were mostly hard work so I don't have a particularly strong connection to my past.

I struggled to interact with my own peers, or most people in most scenarios for that matter. My memories are awkward or frustrating—more like a jagged road full of potholes simply getting me to this point.

From an early age I felt like I couldn't be myself because people wouldn't accept or tolerate me. From the beginning, I looked for ways to regulate and calm the stress that would seep through my body from my overloaded senses. In moments of stress (as simple as an unexpected conversation) I would look to regulate my heightened stress by running my fingers over shapes I saw, or tracing letters of a word in my head or by tracing around my nails repeatedly. Self-soothing or calming (or stimming as I'll explain shortly) is still a huge part of my coping mechanism to this day and always will be.

When I was young, I enjoyed leaving the house in a three-piece suit: pants, vest and a proper jacket. I can't explain this fashion choice but my sense of fashion has always been different. I'm the first to acknowledge my fashion sense has had its ups and downs over the years but it always made sense to me.

What didn't make sense to me were school photos. Mine are made up of either a confused fake smile or an angry looking kid with an eyebrow up asking, *What the hell is this all about? I wait in line to sit down for two seconds so this moment can be captured forever.* Do parents not realise that they can take photos of their children in their school uniform at home, under controlled conditions? What kind of weird conspiracy is this whole school photo thing anyway?"

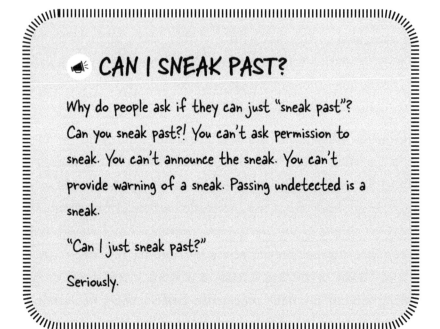

### 📢 CAN I SNEAK PAST?

Why do people ask if they can just "sneak past"? Can you sneak past?! You can't ask permission to sneak. You can't announce the sneak. You can't provide warning of a sneak. Passing undetected is a sneak.

"Can I just sneak past?"

Seriously.

Growing up as an Autistic child was tricky, especially an undiagnosed Autistic child. I'm part of a lost generation that was labelled as different and difficult because there were no other words that fit. I didn't present like a typical Autistic person "should" in the time of my childhood, which was the one-size-fits-all white boy with severe or profound challenges.

It was my literal sense of communication that shocked people, my bluntness that cost me friendships, my anxiety that made me go to the toilet repeatedly before leaving the house, my rebuttals and defiance to parental requests and instructions, comments and opinions that were seen as me being a smartass, my need and preference for alone time and routine, my inability to tolerate certain foods due to consistency or smell (pumpkin makes me gag, but I like pumpkin soup. The smell of peas makes me sick, yet I like pea and ham soup).

I grew up in a working/lower middle-class family but I never felt like I went without. My parents did an amazing job raising so many kids and providing for us. I could not raise five kids. Keeping two kids alive is hard enough. I had the best parents and family, and I believe they did the best job they could, but I still felt like the odd man out.

My mum was born in Canada and our relationships with that side of the family were distant during my childhood however this changed for me later in life. Fortunately, my relationship with my dad's parents was something very special; I was crazy close to them growing up. Particularly with my nan; the most wonderful, kind and funny lady.

I would spend school holidays (and many other times in between) staying with her and Pop. We would go to the shops and the movies and it felt like it was my time, doing fun things my way because Nan supported me in what I did, and how I did it. When I was a little older, she even organised work experience for me at the local radio station. Though I'm pretty sure my Pop was a Freemason and may have secretly run the town from his loungeroom recliner. Let's just call it a team effort.

## A SONG AND DANCE

Nan's favourite stories to tell were of me putting on shows in the shopping centre. Little song and dance shows that attracted a crowd of old ladies thinking how cute it was, this little 5-year-old in a suit putting on a cabaret show. I don't remember the shows, but I know I got my inspiration from watching those old matinee movies with stars like Gene Kelly or Doris Day. My Pop would put them on for us and I think that's why I love those old movies to this day.

Even Mum has told me if they ever lost me in the shopping centre, they'd just have to look for a crowd to find me entertaining people. Looking back, armed with what I know now, this was my way of interacting: by not interacting directly. The crowd stood back and watched my little song and dance in a cute suit, they clapped and smiled but I didn't otherwise need anything from them, it was a straightforward transaction, with clear direction and signals, without any puzzling actions or words from anyone.

Nan loved and connected with my shows; I remember how often and fondly she spoke of them. My strongest memories are her telling me all about my great shows! Those little performances and Nan's support were incredible moments of growth for me.

> **My whole career in content and entertainment can be traced back to her positive reinforcement at critical times in my young life.**

So that was the high point. The low point revolves a lot around school and in a nutshell, I hated it. Not the learning; it was the sensory overload, the stress and anxiety overload, the awkward nature of standing out, even when I was trying not to. In primary school the bullying could be pushes and punches on the bus, while in high school it was more mental and malicious.

My primary school years were a mixed bag of high highs and low lows, with no in between. The two things that could connect me to people and save me from bullying, at least temporarily, were my sense of humour and my freakish running speed. I could outrun any kid at school, any time. I was fast in an unnatural sense. There may be a speed demon inside me. Just saying.

I struggled with adapting to new teachers, new classrooms, and different environmental settings. One classroom was big and freezing cold, while another was small and stuffy. Some felt safe, and others overstimulated my senses to the point of shutdown or meltdown. And don't get me started on adjoining classrooms.

I quickly realised that this school thing just wasn't working for me like everyone else. To start with, I struggled to form a friendship group like most kids I saw were doing. The one or two friendships I did have kept exploding into, "What did you say/do that for Orion?" when I hadn't realised what I said was wrong. I would say how sorry I was but then bang! It was over, my bridge burnt. It felt like I was in a foreign country, not knowing the language but trying to maintain relationships, it just didn't make any sense.

On one hand, this confusion and constant uncertainty in relationships around me created a disconnect that means as an adult I am not nostalgic about most of my formative years. Though I do look fondly on the time a friend in primary school started the—and this is a direct quote—"'Orion's a bastard' club." True story.

However, there is another important side to these friendships-gone-wrong that is always with me. I remember a high school art class I was in; I can still clearly see the desks shaped like an L. A friend of mine seated in front of me was doing something he shouldn't do and when I brought everyone's attention to it by exclaiming something, this accidentally got my friend in trouble. I remember him looking back at me in shock, as he fired at me in the voice of Daffy Duck, "You're despicable!"

That's the thing about an Autistic childhood. No matter what you do or how hard you try, people will still label you hard work. I am the rude, offensive, crap friend. Imagine spending your childhood suppressing your true self to make others feel comfortable and still failing every single day.

And you know what? Those confusing conversations, the broken friendships, the issues that I had as a child, all still plague me today, because (bombshell) you do not grow out of autism. I will never mentally recover from the consequences of when I offended or hurt someone's feelings just by being a watered-down version of me. I still lose sleep thinking back over countless moments and events in my life where friendships, relationships and opportunities have blown up in my face. Those scars are real.

## 📢 IF I'M HONEST

I don't get why people say, "If I'm honest." If you are honest. Seriously, saying "If I'm honest" before you say something means you're telling me for the most part you're a bloody liar, but now, "If I have to be, I'll be honest." So, what you're really saying is I'm not an honest person, I'm not trustworthy, in fact I'm a complete pathological liar, but if I was honest, I would probably say something like this.

Here's an idea, be honest all the time.

From an early age I often struggled to relate to my siblings, and looking back I'd say that my parents had a very different experience parenting me. Not dissimilar to my experience as a father today. I didn't tend to get in too much trouble at school (unlike some of my siblings) but in my mind, it felt like my parents still saw me as the hard kid to raise. In my mind it was like they were backing the wrong horse, but maybe as an undiagnosed Autistic child, I was unbackable. Others may have considered me different and difficult, as though I deliberately behaved in a way that baffled, frustrated, triggered and exhausted my parents.

This created endless frustration, and underneath maybe some resentment too; of me, or the cards they were dealt; you can argue it anyway you want. Who can blame them for shipping me off to my grandparents' house? They clearly needed a rest from me. And now that I'm a father of an Autistic child I can completely relate to what they must have been feeling and experiencing.

It's extraordinary to think how good a job my parents did considering the challenges of raising five children. In fact, they actually had six children. Six! I struggle managing two! And my wife struggles managing three. ⟶ Which includes me.

My parents suffered enormous heartache early in their parenting life, when they lost my baby sister at just one year old. At the time I was the eldest (around six), then came my two younger sisters. Early one morning, I was lying in bed with Mum and Dad (that all-end-up-in-the-bed kind of night) when they asked me to go and check on my baby sister. Simple task, yes.

But not this day.

When I peered into the cot, my little baby sister wasn't moving, nor was she sleeping; and from memory she looked purple. I didn't emotionally react. I couldn't process it at all. This is a clear Autistic reaction in hindsight. Somehow, I returned to my parents' bedroom and told them in my matter-of-fact way that she wasn't waking up.

The sounds and screams that followed are memories I will never forget. The ambulance came, everyone was crying.

But me; I was blank, I was numb, no processing took place at the time. I was confronted and disorientated by the unfamiliar noises and events racing around me that I could only walk around quietly trying to make sense of what was going on. I later learnt that my baby sister had basically choked during the night from some food she had coughed up in her sleep. Such a freakish series of events made processing it all even harder.

When I look back, it's extraordinary how this loss didn't break my parents. They did a phenomenal job continuing on, growing and nurturing their family further, and I thank them eternally for that.

Personally, it wasn't until I was in one of my first acting classes in 2010, that I had a scene that needed heavy emotion and somehow, with no conscious intention, that event from my past came rushing to the present moment and my character ended up screaming and crying with 30 years of grief finally finding a way out. The other students watching were left speechless; how could they know they were witnessing real grief being processed long after the event happened?

You might wonder why I have shared a story of sorrow with you but I have two clear objectives. Firstly, is to pay **homage to my parents** and their strength to continue on and make a loving home for the rest of their children, which they absolutely did.

A loving home however, can't stop the endless frustration of trying to get the world to accept you. If my parents found me hard at home, a place I could theoretically be myself, what hope was there in the outside world? There was no reason or excuse in their eyes (and wider society of course too) for offending people, being rude or making people upset.

Even if I had had a diagnosis growing up, this would still have been the case because this is still the perspective people often take today when they say, "Being Autistic is no excuse for being rude, raw or too honest."

> **Being Autistic is not an excuse;**
> **it's a reason for how we are different.**

However, truly understanding autism means recognising it comes with unique behavioural traits, challenges and strengths that are hardwired into our different brain. All the years of suppressing, masking and pretending to be "normal" is profoundly exhausting and debilitating (even incapacitating) for an Autistic person.

It's like being an actor on set but the scene never ends, no one yells "Cut!" It mentally and physically cannot be done. Autistic behaviours are natural actions and responses to the way we view the world according to the unique brain we were born with—an Autistic brain!

We don't set out to offend or upset or frustrate. Endorsing a narrow mindset such as, "Autism is no excuse for that response or this behaviour" is a view I won't accept and will continue to debunk until the day I die.

> If you go by the stats, this isn't far away!

I will fight to change the hearts and minds of wider society to look beyond the behaviour of Autistic people they find uncomfortable or unacceptable, and help them understand the basis of it.

I will continue to fight for wider understanding behind:

- Why we must try and regulate our environment.
- Why it's critical for us to self soothe through stimming.
- Why we can become obsessed with a subject or interest.
- Why it's helpful and downright obvious to point out errors.
- Why solving the problems of others is our first response.

These are not excuses for behaviour; they are reasons.

**There is always an irrefutable reason behind an Autistic person's actions and motivations.**

Over time, I have benefitted from the knowledge of my own childhood (and hindsight), as my wife and I raise our two sons, one being Autistic like me. The difference for him particularly is that my wife and I have sought assistance, a diagnosis and practical help for him and the family as a whole.

The help and resources for parenting Autistic children is growing rapidly and gives everyone courage and faith in a new acceptance and respect going forward. I must point out however, that it is critical that Autistic people with their lived experiences take the lead in this space.

The other reason I shared the story of my little sister was to point out the simple fact that traumatic events (or parenting in some cases) *do not* cause autism. Walking into that scene did not make me Autistic. It certainly could have given me PTSD but autism cannot be acquired, caught or caused later in life. My reaction and delayed processing in this event illustrate the difference; that's the proof.

You are either born Autistic or you are not. Unfortunately for me it was decades after my birth that I was finally recognised as Autistic. To be clear, going undiagnosed for so long had a catastrophic impact on my career in radio, and my ability to maintain meaningful relationships.

In fact, I firmly believe, even if previous employers, friends or partners of mine read this book and actually digest it, they will think no differently of me and continue to hold the view that I am just a bad person.

**In saying that, receiving my autism diagnosis was one of the best days of my life.**

# CHAPTER 2 | MY ADULT DIAGNOSIS

D o you wonder if you or someone you know could be Autistic? I'm confident you'll find some answers, hope or support in the story of my adult diagnosis.

I have always felt different and I just assumed (which may seem ridiculous to you) that I was simply a bad person, a misfit who didn't belong or deserve to be here. I thought I wasn't a very good person or friend or worker; not a very good *anything*. I felt that there was something different about me that always created roadblocks or snags in everyday (neurotypical) life.

It wasn't just the occasional moment; I'm talking about daily, minute-by-minute issues with friendships, relationships, social interactions, studying, working, and really every facet of modern-day life. It reached the point where I started to think, *Hang on, life is not supposed to be this hard, why is mine?* I had to try to understand because I'd had enough. If I was born to suffer through life, I'd had enough. I'd reached my threshold for blindly suffering through life. I wanted answers either way.

People often ask me why I sought a diagnosis. Sometimes they tell me, "I wouldn't have picked you for being Autistic," or "You don't look Autistic." Well, I wouldn't have picked you for being so bloody ignorant but here we are—there is no look. The only Autistic thing about an Autistic person is their brain.

But I'm going to put my manners back in and walk you through it. I know what you're thinking, *You're married, have two kids and have had a successful career in media.* If by successful, you mean years of struggling to fit into teams and workplaces then yes, I've made it this far. So even if I was Autistic, you may argue surely it's only a light sprinkling of autism with a dash of anxiety? You're wondering, *What would be the point of getting a diagnosis at this stage of your life?*

*Mental telepathy is a perk of having an Autistic brain.*

I wish it were that easy. Sure, I have achieved all those things and have a great life. However, each day my life is still weighed down, and riddled with significant challenges. I've always loved and been good at what I do for work but on the flip side I've struggled to fit into workplaces.

Prior to meeting my wife, I had a string of failed relationships and friendships. And since we've had kids, I've found parenting in the neurotypical sense (non-Autistic) a constant challenge. And don't get me started on trying to study at university as a mature-age Autistic person! I'll go into how that imploded further down the track.

It wasn't just my many challenges that led me to an assessment for Autism. It was also my "quirky" behaviours or traits I have and didn't even realise were Autistic traits. I'm that guy people tend to label nervous, fidgety, and restless. I now know that what I was actually doing was stimming, which is a form of self-stimulation or regulation used by Autistic people. Without always realising it, I pull my hair, rub my fingers, trace things with my eyes and fingers, break into song or put on a funny voice.

**These are all ways I make sense of the alien world around me and bring myself back to a comfortable place.**

On a lighter note, you'll be happy to hear that all my forms of stimming trigger and set off my Autistic son and vice versa. So that's ideal…

Other Autistic traits of mine include being just terrible at social interaction, or understanding verbal and non-verbal cues and conventions. Also, it might sound harmless but as you probably know by now, I am always honest. Most neurotypical people would say I am brutally honest. But the way I see it, you are either honest or dishonest and it only feels brutal when it's true.

No one ever complains about being told the truth when they agree with it or accept it. Even the truth is broken down by neurotypical people into good and bad subcategories. And while we're at it, there is no such thing as "my truth." I don't want to hear "your truth," I just want the truth. You, on the other hand, can't handle the truth.

Another clear trait I have is a hypersensitivity to sensory things including sounds, smells, light, criticism, and my favourite, people who are in your face from the get-go. Seriously, give me some time to warm up. Now pay attention because I'm only going to write this once... Sure, you can re-read it.

In my experience as an Autistic person with an Autistic son, I can confidently say that we need more time to process and adjust to people entering our space. People who do not give me that time rarely get a second chance. It's not personal. It's about us and our need to maintain an environment free of hypersensitivity triggers. In essence it's about following our energy and cues, giving us time and space to regulate ourselves in an ever-changing environment and dynamic.

*Hey! Who's writing this book?!*

You can be you, just understand that no matter who you are to an Autistic person or how well you know them, having you enter their space requires processing, adjustment and regulation. And please don't take the often indifferent greeting personally. We feel that way about everyone. Disdain is my default greeting. That line still makes me laugh. —> *Please laugh.*

One characteristic you may notice about Autistic people is a laser-focused passion (bordering on obsession) for a particular thing or subject. I don't want to provide examples as it perpetuates damaging myths and misconceptions about Autistic people. For me, my passion is entertaining and communicating: radio, podcasts, YouTube videos and blogs (and now this book) are my fixation, sometimes referred to as my special interest, as we'll explore soon.

So what's the difference between a special interest and a hobby? Good question Orion. → Thank you Orion.

A hobby is generally something neurotypical people do when they have spare time for relaxation and recreation. (Fun fact: in Australia some sporting grounds are called recreation reserves, or rec reserves for short, which comes from the reservation of Crown Land for recreation—thanks law school.) Put simply, hobbies are things people do in their spare time to relax, unwind and socialise.

A special interest is often an Autistic person's whole life. Autistic people may only want to spend their day on their special interest. I would choose doing my special interest and creating content over basic self-care like eating, drinking, sleeping, showering, going to the toilet, and taking breaks. For me, everyone and everything gets in the way of my special interest. I don't do it to unwind or socialise, I do it because it is my life blood.

Prior to having any idea about what all these factors meant, let alone knowing they were Autistic traits, I was experiencing high levels of anxiety on a daily basis and to a lesser extent I was also weighed down by depression. Feeling like I was in the world but not part of it was starting to erode what feeling of belonging I had found with my wife. I didn't have a place in the world, didn't feel part of things—family, friendships or work groups. Life still felt surreal, like I hadn't joined in yet or I was never a part of it.

The anxiety was killing me and my quality of life was really getting me down. This is the part where I proudly get to say loudly and clearly, **"Thank God for my wife!"**

I would have kept on thinking, *I'm a bad person. I was born to suffer; I'll suffer and then I'll die.* My wife's extraordinary support got me to a GP (family doctor) where we talked holistically about the situation and the journey really took flight.

So with the continuing support of my wife, I went through a maze of doctors and specialists: a GP, a clinical psychologist, a psychiatrist and eventually a Professor of Psychiatry who focuses and specialises in autism. All that went into a melting pot and then at the end, "Hey, congratulations, you're Autistic!" No.

If only that was my experience—but it wasn't as straightforward and easy as that. Initially, when the possibility of autism was brought up at my very first therapy session it really rattled me because I was seeking help for my serious anxiety; the referral clearly stated depression and anxiety. However, the psychologist picked up on some points just from our interaction and raised the idea of autism within our first discussions.

After the surprise of where the conversation was going, a few suspicions started hovering around my mind and I knew I wanted to follow it further. I still see that same psychologist today and am endlessly grateful to have found her. I really believe every Autistic person should see a psychologist and enter into some form of therapy for as long as they can.

**Mental health will be one of the biggest challenges faced by an Autistic person in their lifetime.**

Next comes a warning scenario for anyone in a similar position to the one I found myself in. I was initially referred to a local psychiatrist who by the end of the consultation (if that's what you want to call it), left me feeling more depressed and lost than I'd ever been in my life. My wife later told me she feared for my life. Let me tell you why.

To begin with, through almost the entire consultation this psychiatrist kept yawning into his hand, completely disinterested. Then at the end of the cold consultation he blandly said, "Look, on and off intermittently in this conversation, you've made some eye contact so you can't be Autistic; you've spoken about how you've studied at university; you can't be Autistic."

Everything about me right down to my ability to speak well was cited as clear evidence against an autism diagnosis. At the time I knew little about autism, but I have since learnt that the current medical model used to view autism is straight out of the 1960s.

From my point of view I was surprised by the adamant dismissal at the time, but I thought, *Well... he's the psychiatrist, he knows what he's talking about.* I put no weight on my own instincts, on my own gut feeling. Not listening to my intuition was severely detrimental to my mental health.

In effect, the experience with that psychiatrist validated my belief that I was simply a bad person who was just born to suffer. My wife saw how this experience affected me and was extremely concerned for my mental health; she could see I was just at such a loss and couldn't see any light or way out of the state I was in.

She encouraged me to seek a second opinion, find someone to take the assessment seriously and actually give it the time it requires. At first I didn't want to waste my time, the last thing I needed was another experience that reinforced my perception that I was just a bad person. Why would I want to go through that again?

**As you read this, consider how many people, some just children, are being let down and misdiagnosed by a system that leaves them behind.**

Fortunately for me, my wife was really passionate about giving it a second chance and persistent as well. After a while I got a referral for a second psychiatrist and this time round, the psychiatrist was a professor in his field and had a genuine interest and specialty in autism. From the first moment it was a completely different experience. There were multiple consultations through a whole phase of different forms of assessment and testing and conversations and history.

It might sound strange but I really enjoyed it. The experience was really rewarding; I was finally taken seriously; finally heard. And again, I can only answer the questions, do the assessments, do the tests, have the conversations, and give the history. That's all I can do. In other words I wasn't doctor shopping until I found one willing to give me what I wanted. My wife was at every consultation with me and contributed many experiences (similar to what a parent would do in a child's diagnosis). There was no show, no act, just me allowing my true self to be seen and heard.

At the end of the lengthy process, this psychiatrist diagnosed me as Autistic. In fact, he also diagnosed me with two forms of anxiety. It was simply the most rewarding weight lifted off my shoulders. Being diagnosed as Autistic by a psychiatrist specialising in Autism was a giant relief. I felt so much lighter and instantly happier.

> **It dawned on me that I had lived two lives.**
> **My life as an undiagnosed Autistic person and**
> **my life post-diagnosis.**

In my mind they were two different people. For the first time in my life I didn't just see myself as a bad person. I now had an idea of why I am the way I am. From there my perspective could only keep growing as I continued to learn more about the real Autistic me. This knowledge became a catalyst for practical, intellectual, and welcome adjustments that drastically increased my quality of life. Without a doubt the mental health benefits of a diagnosis were immeasurable. Not to mention the benefits to my relationship with my wife and kids.

# BENEFITS OF A DIAGNOSIS

A diagnosis is akin to a rebirth. You live the first part of your life not knowing who you are while being aware you're trying to be someone you're not: neurotypical. Being an undiagnosed Autistic person is like swimming against an endless tide of challenges you don't understand:

- Sensory overload.
- Social brick walls and rejections.
- Education and workplace hurdles and challenges.
- Resentment from personal and professional directions.
- Strange, disapproving looks.
- Angry, insensitive comments.
- Dismissive responses and interactions.
- Constant expectations that seem to shake the foundations of the stable ground you need for survival.

Imagine waking up every morning with the expectation that society demands you do everything their way even though it goes against every instinct your brain is screaming at you, added to the fact that it's neurologically impossible. You can't tell a PC to be a Mac. You can't tell a dog to be a cat. Yet here we are. And for completeness I've checked and there is no switch on my brain to turn off the autism.

Finally to all this, you are then told (if you are one of the lucky ones to navigate waiting lists, high costs, and gender bias) you're actually Autistic and there comes an "Aha" moment. So despite all your efforts to fit in and please neurotypical people, you never could have succeeded because fundamentally you are *not* neurotypical; your brain won't allow it because you're Autistic. **It's your identity.** Receiving a diagnosis means you are given the freedom of your true identity. In fact, I view it as a recognition rather than a diagnosis. I was born Autistic, it just hadn't been recognised until later in life.

> The simple act of acceptance and support from your family and friends can be the biggest benefit of receiving an autism diagnosis... It can also be the hardest thing to achieve.

In my case it was a series of mixed reactions, some supportive, some undecided, and some outright rejection of the diagnosis. As an Autistic person with an Autistic son I can see this from both sides. Frankly, it's understandable that some members of your family may be the last to accept your diagnosis, but I feel that comes from a place of guilt (which is not justified, they did the best they could), and a basic lack of knowledge around autism (which again is not intentional).

Autistic people should accept that their family and friends are, for the most part, simply pre-enlightened. While the family and friends of newly diagnosed Autistic people are responsible for increasing their understanding and acceptance of autism post-diagnosis.

> Yes, it is your responsibility to educate yourself about autism to better understand and support the Autistic person in your life, not theirs.

Since my diagnosis, I have continually sought greater education and self-awareness as an Autistic person. My diagnosis allowed me to acknowledge my needs and vulnerabilities to myself and the important people in my life. It allows me to know and facilitate what I need when I meet new people. But I don't want you to think of this as something that is just beneficial for me. Understanding the triggers and support needs of the Autistic person in your life is mutually beneficial. It's a win-win. Simply put, increasing the quality of life and mental health of the Autistic person in your life can only have the same effect on you.

Even more exciting, my diagnosis created an enormous opportunity for me. I channelled and cultivated my unique strength and passion for communicating through content creation, as I never had before. I was fuelled with the purpose to convey my lived experiences and first-hand insights to people all around the world to educate as many people as I can, and advocate for the Autistic community.

Finding this path, this adventure, this quest as it were, that enables me to inform, educate, entertain and communicate to people right across the planet about being Autistic is one of my greatest achievements. It is my purpose; it is my mission.

Quick side note, I have had people claim my content creation and communication skills are direct examples of why I cannot possibly be Autistic. And that's always so nice to hear, very much appreciated. Really great feedback. Let's get this straight. My communication via my content creation is predominately one-sided. It's me talking to me. There is rarely direct communication with others.

And there is a clear difference between my regular content and the content I do with others, including my wife. People even pointed out in the comments that I barely looked my wife in the eyes or showed any insight into her feelings or emotions.

But how can this be? Because I'm Autistic! I have significant challenges with social interaction and communication.

# POST-DIAGNOSIS CHALLENGES

Along with the benefits, come the challenges of receiving an adult diagnosis (if there weren't any, you probably wouldn't be reading this book). Being diagnosed as an adult could be viewed as nothing more than receiving a piece of paper. You aren't referred to any real support or services to improve your life. You're just told by a medical professional that you are Autistic and sent on your way to live in an Autistic utopia.

Here's the thing, for kids who are diagnosed Autistic in Australia, there are varying levels of government funding and support available. Support services include occupational therapists, speech pathologists, psychologists and any other -ists you can think of. Both my Autistic son and I are supported by the NDIS (National Disability Insurance Scheme) in Australia.

For children like my son, the majority of supports fall under the umbrella term "Early Intervention Therapies." What a horrible name for services aimed at children. They're not addicted to drugs or alcohol. They don't need an intervention.

Isn't the point of an intervention to intervene and change a person for the better? Are we really intervening on Autistic children to change them into neurotypical children? Because that's not only neurologically impossible, it's also manifestly damaging to the children involved.

Whatever way you look at it, support services for Autistic children are geared towards rendering them indistinguishable from their neurotypical peers. Autistic children get acting classes, while Autistic adults get shown the stage door.

An adult diagnosis, in my experience, leaves you feeling the same as you did before; like an outcast, someone who was just meant to drift through life, a loner, feeling out of place, like a misfit, or an alien. A diagnosis doesn't take away those feelings; the only difference is now you know you're Autistic. And you realise you'll still have those same feelings even though no one's willing or able to provide you with the help and support you may need.

Too many supports and therapies for Autistic adults are generic, one-size-fits-all services. Yet it is now widely known that autism is a spectrum, where no two Autistic people are the same; it's not linear. It's an infinite spectrum of varying challenges, strengths and care and support needs, more like the variety and depth found in a colour wheel.

One of the biggest post-diagnosis challenges for me that most people don't realise is that my (unique and individual) diagnosis means that I do require daily support to live my life in a neurotypical world. It doesn't mean that I require the same level of care and support as other Autistic people, but it absolutely does still indicate that I require daily support. I'm also a firm believer that the care and support needs of Autistic people are fluid. Again, some Autistic people will have higher support needs than others, but in my view the support needs of all Autistic people can fluctuate daily.

In short, I am still where I was prior to my diagnosis, sent off with a vague, "Best of luck, mate. Hope your life goes okay." In a sense nothing much changes to the outside world. You don't get a fresh start or second chance even though you were living your life with an undiagnosed disability. In my experience, society doesn't want to see it through any other lens than the one they are used to looking through. They see you as someone constantly trying and failing to be neurotypical, "No, no, it's just you, you're still the same bad person."

And I just don't understand it. A medical professional has confirmed on the record that I'm Autistic and require daily support in living my life in a neurotypical world but not everyone accepts it or shows support for that. It doesn't make any sense to me. They refuse to take the diagnosis for what it means, there is no revelation, "Oh wow, okay, I get it now. That's why you behaved like this, or did that in that situation, because you're Autistic. I can see you through this lens now."

It grates on you to receive a diagnosis and then have people overlook it and still judge you through the lens of being neurotypical, something you cannot succeed at when you were born Autistic.

You might be disheartened by now and wondering, *What's the point of getting a diagnosis?* And there is value in asking that question so you don't rush in for the wrong reasons. You can now see there are absolutely post-diagnosis benefits and challenges, just like there are challenges and benefits of being neurotypical. I am not about being positive or negative. I'm about being real; I'm about being true, honest, open, raw. We're never going to get people to understand and accept Autistic people if we live in a fairytale land.

It's not my problem if you can't deal with me and my differences. It is my goal though, to do the best I can to be as raw and open and honest as anyone can be to hopefully cultivate some understanding and acceptance of not only me, but Autistic people right across the planet.

## 📣 THE 2000s

We really have to get to the bottom of why people still refer to the present year as two thousand and something. They are saying it wrong. Let's say you know someone who was born in 1998. If you asked them what year they were born, they're going to say they were born in the year nineteen ninety-eight. Yet here we are in a new century and instead of saying twenty like we said nineteen last century, people are saying two thousand.

It's twenty! If you don't think it is, next time someone asks you if you were born in 1985, or whenever someone references the last century as nineteen something, be sure to tell them they're saying it wrong. Tell them the correct way is to say, "One thousand, nine hundred and eighty five."

See how that goes for you.

# CHAPTER 3

# AUTISM FACTS

*You need to know!*

You may have gathered by now that I'm a perpetual information seeker. Intensely inquisitive if you will. My diagnosis set in motion the biggest research assignment of my life (and I went to law school and almost graduated).

I didn't know the first thing about autism, let alone any other disability, so early on it was a steep learning curve with many wrong turns and misinformation. I read every piece of information and digested any content I could find about autism, be that neurologically, historically, behaviourally, educationally, socially, globally and every anecdote or lived experience in between.

Everything I have gathered (besides not being able to fit into this book) reflects my own personal journey of self-discovery and enlightenment. Every Autistic person is different in infinite ways that's why it's a spectrum, so the information I present here is based on my own research, opinions and most of all my lived experience as an Autistic guy with an Autistic son.

Now that I've delighted and amazed you with my adult diagnosis story, let's start to break down what we know and think we know (but often can't know unless we ask),

*Oh, and another little dude and one amazing wife.*

about autism and Autistic individuals from a wider perspective. This section is intended to open your eyes to the must-know facts about autism, and some of the myths and misconceptions we are burdened with. Some of these misconceptions can be extremely hurtful and potentially harmful to an Autistic person's mental health and quality of life, so I'm here to bust some myths with my world famous bare-all style and grace.

Let's start with some of the most important facts on autism that you absolutely need to know, so you can then start breaking down those misconceptions in your community.

# AUTISM FACTS

### FACT 1:

AUTISM IS NOT A DISEASE AND CANNOT BE CURED

Autism cannot be cured because it is not a disease. Essentially, some neurotypical people have tried to perpetuate the myth that autism is a disease that can and should be cured, as though autism is undesirable, or bad and a cure can fix it.

However, autism is a neurological, developmental difference; a medically diagnosed disability acknowledging an Autistic person has a different brain. Our brains are wired differently, simple as that, nothing else makes us Autistic. Perpetuating the myth that autism can be cured displays an attitude and ignorance that doesn't help anyone, in fact it's actually really harmful. No matter what someone's motivations are behind this idea, it actually can't be achieved. **You cannot cure the incurable.** You may think it's in the best interest of your child to fix or alter them. But how would you react to the concept that you are essentially broken or bad and you need to be fixed?

Autism is not a disease that grows or develops in the brain after you are born. My Autistic brain was formed in the womb along with my fingers and toes, all uniquely mine with different fingerprints to every other human being, and similarly a uniquely different brain! I was born Autistic, I will die Autistic.

## FACT 2:

### AUTISM HAS A GENETIC LINK

Autistic people have a different brain and clearly the brain is a tough thing to study and understand. So brain science is an ever-changing landscape, which means the difference between an Autistic brain, and a neurotypical brain continues to be explored, researched and learnt from. As we move through new levels of understanding, it has been established there is a clear link between genetics and autism.[3] Autism is often genetic.

I can use my own experience to illustrate one of the most obvious examples of this genetic link. Sometimes when an adult is diagnosed as Autistic, it occurs around the same time as, or as a result of, one of their children being diagnosed. Somewhere along the process of your child being assessed, there can be a "Me too," or "Aha" moment and you realise, *Hmm, this seems pretty familiar to me, I'm relating to a lot of what's going on here, maybe I am Autistic too.*

You feel impelled to get assessed and ultimately you may receive the diagnosis, but you weren't diagnosed just because your son or daughter was; you were always Autistic. You went on to have a child, that child had a genetic link and was born Autistic just like you. This might not be something you want to hear, but if you are a parent of an Autistic child or a grandparent of an Autistic child, chances are one of you are also Autistic. It's just plain genetics 101.

Remember, you cannot catch or acquire autism through your life. It isn't caused by a bad childhood or some weird life experiences. It is a lifelong state of being from the moment you are born.

## FACT 3:

### AUTISM IS NOT AN INTELLECTUAL DISABILITY

Autism is not an intellectual disability; it is a neuro-developmental disability. There's a difference between being Autistic and having an intellectual disability. In my opinion, the idea that being Autistic automatically means you have an intellectual disability comes from the medical or deficit-based model of viewing Autistic people. Looking at the diagnostic criteria (such as those used in the DSM-5[4]) it simply comes down to a checklist of what Autistic people can't do.

**"Can we build a case that this person has enough deficits of things they can't do in a neurotypical world to therefore diagnose them as Autistic?"**

So the diagnostic criteria of viewing Autistic people as people with deficits that need to be fixed, improved, altered or intervened upon, is one of the main drivers for society assuming all Autistic people have intellectual disabilities.

There's no real conversation or dialogue about their strengths; about what Autistic people *can* do. Just like the general population, Autistic people can have above average IQs, average IQs, or below average IQs; and some may also have intellectual disabilities. But that in its most common form is a comorbidity, in addition to a diagnosis of being Autistic.

It really isn't that complicated; just like everyone else on the planet, every Autistic person is different. Some are non-speaking, some have intellectual disabilities, some have other comorbidities, and some have above average intelligence. I don't really care what it is. Everyone is as valuable as the next person. We're all just different.

## FACT 4:

IDENTITY-FIRST LANGUAGE IS PREFERRED

In my experience, much of the Autistic community now prefer identity-first language rather than person-first language. We prefer to be referred to as an Autistic person, rather than a person with autism or a person who has autism. Not that those things are wrong if that's your personal choice, I'm just saying the majority of the Autistic community that I have come into contact with in this day and age, have a preference for identity-first language.

I'm Orion and I'm Autistic. I do not *have* autism.

For example, someone might say to you, "I am gay." They don't say, "I have gayness." Do you see what I'm saying? That makes no sense. They *identify* as being gay. Whatever description they want to use, they don't say they have it, they actually are it, it's part of their identity, right? I was born white (Caucasian), but I don't have whiteness. I certainly have freckles and skin damage from the Aussie summers, but that's about it.

If you have a young son or daughter, please, allow them to understand themselves as an Autistic person. That's such an important aspect for people to understand. This applies on a broader scale too, the idea of accepting and understanding autism. Knowledge and acceptance are so important for me to rouse society to move forward in their thinking and attitude to autism.

*I also have movie star looks and a baby face, but you get the idea.*

**To be frank, I hate being Autistic in a world that doesn't care. Autistic people live in a neurotypical world, designed for neurotypical, non-Autistic people. It is not set up for us.**

There are no "mind ramps" (I coined this term to rave reviews and some blank faces) like there are physical ramps for other disabilities. We don't have mind ramps to support and enable an Autistic person to thrive in all environments. Some may refer to this as the need for autism-friendly practices and spaces.

However, in my view even the best practice, autism-friendly models available for implementation are generic and lack sophistication. They are also too often devised by a genuine lack of Autistic people from all walks of life. Too often the world still looks at us as if to say, "It's your fault, you're the broken one. Why should I have to change for you?"

But after all, I've had to buy into your world. I'm living my life as an Autistic person based on the rules, written and unwritten, of the neurotypical world. If I dared to live my life based on the natural instincts of my brain, I'd never keep a job, which in fact, is my reality anyway; I'd never keep friends, and probably be an outcast, which is also my reality anyway.

So I'm lost every way you look at it, but I'm still doing everything this neurotypical world needs me to do. Like engaging (unsuccessfully) in small talk, forcing myself to make eye contact, fighting the need to stim, and suppressing my true Autistic self to conform to arbitrary neurotypical expectations. It's not like I'm not doing my bit. The question is: when are you going to do yours? Using identity-first language is a great start. I'm Orion and I *am* Autistic.

## FACT 5:

### WE REJECT "FUNCTIONING" LABELS

Functioning labels, as in "high" or "low" functioning autism, are inappropriate and detrimental. I reject functioning labels as they minimise the experiences of some Autistic people, and the potential of others. All Autistic people have individual challenges and strengths and can experience varying capabilities each day. Functioning labels can be unsuspectingly harmful. Let's say that you watch one of my videos and you think to yourself, *Oh, it looks like Orion must be a high functioning Autistic person*. Actually, you probably would have said he has high functioning autism up until reading the previous section. ⟶ You're welcome!

Now, I may appear high functioning to you from watching my videos and listening to my podcasts but that's an observation you're making based on a short piece of produced and edited content, (from a snapshot in time) that has been used as the sole evidence in your judgement of my day-to-day life.

You can't know the challenges I face on a daily basis, nor should you. This isn't about me. This is about the impact functioning labels can have on Autistic people, including young children. When you say an Autistic person is low functioning, it implies (even unintentionally) that they have little to contribute, to achieve, or experiences and perspectives we could learn from; that is utterly and completely wrong. Pigeonholing an Autistic person with a low functioning label, outright denies their contribution and their strengths. Sure they have challenges, but they also have strengths.

Conversely, labelling an Autistic person as high functioning utterly disregards any of their challenges and daily support needs. Either way it doesn't help the community appreciate the unique perspective, challenges, and strengths of each individual Autistic person.

Once again, this shows us that the idea that there is some sort of linear spectrum to autism, a line to judge high functioning, low functioning and in-between, is fanciful, it's wrong, it just doesn't work like that. One minute of a day, I could be really struggling to navigate life in a neurotypical world without some support, and another minute of the day, I could be doing amazing things and appear high functioning to the untrained eye. Bottom line, it's not one or the other, it's fluid.

Connecting an Autistic person's support and care needs with functioning labels is a false and unhelpful link. It also takes away from all their potential, their passion, their ambitions, their achievements and especially their strengths that must be acknowledged and nurtured. Functioning labels minimise the experiences, potential and capabilities of Autistic people, which is unhelpful to everyone.

## FACT 6:

**APPLIED BEHAVIOUR ANALYSIS SUPPRESSES AUTISTIC PEOPLE'S TRUE SELVES**

Applied Behaviour Analysis (ABA)[5] is a so-called therapy designed to change the behaviour of an Autistic person. Essentially, ABA seeks to suppress the natural and unique behaviours of Autistic children and render them indistinguishable from their neurotypical peers.

ABA is basically designed to teach Autistic kids to suppress their true, genuine Autistic selves, a doctrine that I consider to be fraught with issues that endanger the child's sense of identity and self-knowledge and acceptance. Self-awareness and a positive self-image is something they will desperately need to learn and hold onto, as they face the challenges of becoming an Autistic adult in a neurotypical world.

Intervention therapies, which are orthodox, coach Autistic children how to suppress and conform while dumping a massive mental load on what is already an overburdened Autistic child learning about the world around them. Lesson after lesson, therapy session after therapy session, they are guided to build a mask to wear to essentially come across neurotypical. This treatment is also indirectly teaching Autistic people how to camouflage their Autistic traits. Or to paint a stark picture, it's a therapy for parents to send their Autistic kids to so they can be taught how to act neurotypical and be discouraged to ever allow their own genuine traits to come out, to be shown, to be proud of. This, to me, is just heartbreaking.

> **Every Autistic person is entitled to the same rights and freedoms as any other person on the planet, yet here we are in a modern world where Autistic people are viewed as a subgroup of human beings.**

To be clear, there are forms of therapies that are absolutely practical and invaluable to Autistic children and Autistic adults for that matter. There are practical, sensitive methods that have an applied sense in improving the quality of lives of Autistic people. So I'm not talking about all therapies, I'm simply raising your awareness of behavioural therapies whose underlying aim is to teach Autistic people how to suppress their true Autistic selves. They are no more than classes in acting and assimilation.

## FACT 7:

### LIVED EXPERIENCE TRUMPS ALL

The lived experience of an Autistic person trumps all other opinions on autism. It doesn't mean others cannot contribute to understanding autism better and improving the quality of life for Autistic people, that isn't the argument. I'm saying the inclusion of Autistic voices with lived experiences is critical to any discussion on autism.

This is such an important fact yet it hasn't always been a given. Time and again, policies and procedures have been "discussed" and written by non-Autistic voices in positions of authority, and they have a worthy contribution to make. But it doesn't matter what they think they know, what they've studied, what degree they've attained; they finish their discussion on autism, they go home, turn off the autism talk and go back to their "normal" lives.

An Autistic person doesn't get to do that, to switch off the autism; we get the constant, after-hours experience. Again, it's not my intention to offend anyone when I say it's just a fact that neurotypical people do not know what autism is like. You cannot say that you know what autism is like or how it feels because you live or care for an Autistic person. If you're not Autistic, you don't know what living as an Autistic person is like; you don't know because you can't transfer my brain into yours. You might absolutely know what it's like to live with or care for a person who's Autistic and your advocacy is so important, just like my wife advocates for both me and our Autistic son. But it must be acknowledged that it is a very different experience.

For some reason my thoughts on this seem to offend and cause unexpected reactions, including a radio host who couldn't possibly allow me to offend her audience of mothers of Autistic kids. However, the fact is you do NOT have lived experience of autism if you are not Autistic.

## FACT 8:

ALL AUTISTIC PEOPLE COMMUNICATE

All Autistic people communicate, including non-speaking Autistic people, and have a voice that should be heard. The fact that an Autistic person may use other forms of communication, like devices rather than their own voice, doesn't mean they have less to offer, that it's less important or they shouldn't be treated with the same respect as any other person. Autistic people communicate in different ways and every one of them has insights to offer society if we take the time and learn how to listen in their medium, and to give them a chance on their terms.

All Autistic people, no matter how they communicate, should be afforded the same rights and opportunities as all other Autistic people.

## FACT 9:

WE REJECT THE PUZZLE PIECE SYMBOL

In my opinion, the Autistic community largely rejects the puzzle piece symbol as a way of identifying autism. It doesn't matter if your intentions are good or you simply didn't know, ignorance is not a defence. Autistic people do not need to be put back together, or solved, or fixed.

I understand that there are a lot of people who use the puzzle piece symbol with good intentions as a way of identifying autism or their Autistic child, they do it in a proud way, but we have to look at it from the point of view of the Autistic community. Overall, when we look at a puzzle piece, we see something that needs to be put back together, that needs to be solved, that is somehow broken or out of place.

Yet we are not a puzzle. Autistic people are people. Sure, we're different because we have a different brain, but we don't need to be solved or put back together. And for those who are wondering, we largely prefer the infinity loop symbol because it represents the infinite differences of all Autistic people, while celebrating our diversities.

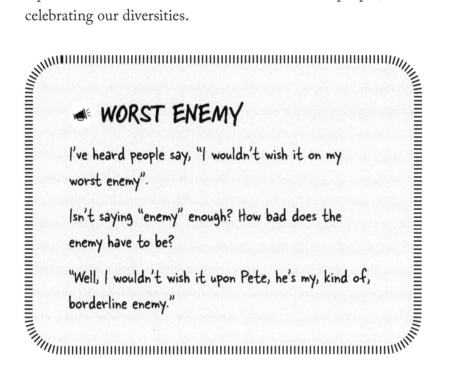

### 📢 WORST ENEMY

I've heard people say, "I wouldn't wish it on my worst enemy".

Isn't saying "enemy" enough? How bad does the enemy have to be?

"Well, I wouldn't wish it upon Pete, he's my, kind of, borderline enemy."

## MYTH BUSTING

This section is dedicated to breaking down some of the most damaging myths and prejudices about autism that I have experienced over the years and still see happening around me. Highlighting and breaking down these misconceptions and assumptions has been much harder to do than I anticipated when I first started recognising and advocating for the challenges, features and qualities around autism.

There were a lot of preconceived notions circulating out there leftover from the Dark Ages that are just so fanciful they're funny. ⟶ In a cry-yourself-to-sleep kind of way.

You might still be clinging on to some of these yourself, and that's okay; I know you're reading this because you want to learn and understand better for yourself, for someone you love and your community, so you're excused—by 10 percent.

## MYTH 1:

### AUTISM CAN BE CAUSED BY BAD PARENTING

This is probably my favourite to talk about because the premise is so ridiculous, it's almost funny. So back in the Dark Ages, there was this theory put out by some dude that cold unemotional parents actually *caused* kids to become Autistic. They called them refrigerator parents because they were considered so cold. The view was these cold, shutdown, emotionless parents somehow created an Autistic child through their bad refrigerator parenting. See what they did there? Refrigerators are cold and so are the... you know what? Forget it.

Since those "simpler" times, we've gone on to discover that's clearly not the case. Sure, poor parenting can certainly have a significant impact on a child's development, identity and mental health. But autism is something you are born with; there is a parental genetic link, and we now know that genetics play quite a significant part in Autistic development in the womb.

As we discussed earlier, sometimes when a child is diagnosed as Autistic one of their parents realises, *Oh, hang on, this is all sounding just like me,* and they themselves go on to receive a diagnosis. Or perhaps a grandparent realises the same thing.

And what you previously thought of as quirky habits or traits in each person, you now understand there's a genetic link just like passing down green eyes to your children. So the idea that bad parenting causes autism is complete rubbish—busted!

## MYTH 2:

### AUTISTIC PEOPLE LACK EMOTIONS AND EMPATHY

In my experience there is a common misconception that Autistic people are often uncaring, unfeeling, cold and do not feel empathy. Many neurotypical people hear the word autism and automatically assume it implies a lack of emotions. This is a myth! Autistic people can in fact be extremely empathetic and absolutely do not lack emotions. We might not be able to process and convey our emotions but trust me, we feel them and we feel them deeply. We are not emotionless robots.

Let's apply some overdue logic on this myth. Today ongoing research into the neurology of a human brain has opened up our understanding that an Autistic brain can struggle to identify, articulate, express or convey emotions the same way as a neurotypical brain. Our brain processes emotions in a different way, but we definitely experience them. Our internal processing of emotions does not necessarily transform into certain words or facial expressions that neurotypical people expect from an interaction or conversation.

When you're engaging in conversation with someone, most of the time you are unconsciously expecting a particular emotion or expression from the other person as the conversation progresses. If a certain reaction isn't received, it's understandable that you're going to think, *Where's the emotion in this guy? Can he hear what I'm saying? Can he feel the pain or joy I'm talking about? He looks indifferent to what I am sharing here!*

In situations where a neurotypical person would expect a certain response—it could be sadness or even humour—an Autistic person, as a general rule, may give little to no response. Their face can remain fairly blank and appear emotionless despite the fact that's not what is actually happening inside us. It's just the manifestation externally. Autistic people can express emotions in many different ways to other people's expectations and, more broadly, societal norms.

> **Our forms of expressing emotion can be unorthodox, unconventional and for some people, unacceptable.**

I get it, I've been there in numerous interactions in numerous settings and workplaces back when I had no knowledge that I was Autistic. Our communication and expression may not be what most people expect. But I've spent my entire life navigating the communication styles of neurotypical people. In the end, it's all about expectations, right? Placing unrealistic expectations on Autistic people to show certain emotions in certain situations is unrealistic and further deepens the damaging misconceptions I see out there.

Throughout my long work life, for as long as I can remember there have been subliminal connotations in common language and behaviour by neurotypical people, that punish and shame Autistic people for their perceived lack of emotions. It may not be intended, but there is often a look, a judgement subtly expressed when a neurotypical person does not receive the response they expect.

Again, I understand why they might feel that way (convention and conditioning), but it is time for the wider community to take responsibility and be informed and respectful of the neurodiversity that the human form comes in. Together we must rise above the blind conditioning and "expectations" we place on each other and commit to re-examining, improving and creating a world where inclusion for all is second nature.

I have seen and experienced these expectations so many times and I know intimately that they not only impact the person going into the conversation with expectations, but the exchange can also affect the mental health of the Autistic person, to the extent of causing potential trauma triggers later in life. Especially if it is an Autistic child experiencing this emotional expectation, judgement and shaming again and again.

In my experience, Autistic people can feel deeper levels of empathy than any other person. Autistic people can, in fact, take on the emotions of other people—be it pain or joy or any emotion—we can take it on, deep into our soul. If I see a baby crying in a stroller or a kid really upset but the adult near them is ignoring them, it really distresses me to the point I actually want to go over there and give that kid a hug. I'm silently begging the adult to stop for five seconds, get down on the child's level and tell them they're going to be okay. Situations like that have a profound effect on me but you might not realise it. Even though we've taken the emotion on internally, our *exterior* can appear emotionless and has therefore given rise to this myth.

Another factor to this myth not to be overlooked is that Autistic people like myself can struggle to actually detect or identify emotions from neurotypical people when they use *implied* communication, such as nonverbal cues, body language, and unspoken actions. These are clues we are often unable to recognise.

Personally, when I am around people, attempting to interact, I am usually unaware that I should be "looking for hints," so I don't see them and therefore, I don't feel what you're saying. You're thinking I *must* have noticed your little signs and so you make a judgement that I am cold and emotionless to your words and state of being. However my world at that moment is taken up with trying to process a million other triggers and emotions, and your cues, body language and unspoken actions are forms of communication not even on my radar.

## MYTH 3:

### AUTISTIC PEOPLE ALL LOOK THE SAME

This next myth is something that I actually experience quite a lot. People might say, "Oh, I wouldn't have picked you for being Autistic," or "You don't look Autistic."

This myth really pushes my buttons and gets me fired up, to presume that in essence Autistic people all look the same or somehow look alike. This supposition refers to physical manifestations, yet autism is nothing more than a neurological difference. We have an Autistic brain rather than a neurotypical brain or a non-Autistic brain (because I understand there are some people who are neither Autistic nor neurotypical). In reality, there is no physical external feature that presents in every Autistic person, unless you are talking about direct relationships and genetically inherited looks, right? We can't all look the same if there's no physical connection to being Autistic—it's a different brain.

All Autistic people are absolutely individual; no two are the same. We all have individual challenges and strengths. Autism isn't specific to one gender or race or geographical location. There's no Autistic "look" aside from the Autistic look I'm giving you right now for thinking this myth exists.↘

Stares menacingly. Then gets distracted by a plane.

## MYTH 4:

### AUTISTIC PEOPLE CAN'T HAVE FRIENDSHIPS OR INTIMATE RELATIONSHIPS

Now let's bust the myth that perpetuates Autistic people can't—or don't want to—establish relationships, friendships or actual intimate relations.

Firstly, let me preface that in my experience, there's no question that Autistic people benefit from assistance and support with social interactions to gain friendships and make connections; it's absolutely required. It's part of the challenge of being Autistic: small talk, interactions, exchanges, listening and understanding how you're supposed to talk to a neurotypical person is a huge hurdle we never stop trying and failing to jump over. After all these years I still struggle to understand why neurotypical people don't like honesty; how can someone be too honest, I ask you?!

The world around us is a hard thing to process. Minute by minute, we're flat out processing not only the world in front of us but the people around us, hearing what they're saying, taking it in, cognition and processing going on and then trying to work out our part in it: *What do I say back? What reaction or facial expression am I supposed to have in this scenario?* The world of relationships is being interpreted through an Autistic brain and everyone's hoping the result comes out neurotypical, yet it doesn't work like that and takes a monumental effort in the process.

Despite the effort it takes, this doesn't mean for a second Autistic people don't value and desire friendships. Learning how neurotypical relationships work is one of those big barriers that keep appearing in many Autistic people's lives; they affect us in every interaction we attempt, in virtually every daily setting as children and they don't stop when we become adults in the workforce or other environments.

> **Understanding why our relationships are not working is a significant barrier to overcome for both Autistic and non-Autistic people.**

I've heard it referred to as the "double empathy" problem, which in essence is the notion that it is not just Autistic people failing to understand or connect with others but a failure of both parties to understand each other.

I'm married and I have two kids, and having a family is one of the greatest things I've ever done in my life; without a doubt one of my greatest achievements. It's also one of the hardest things I've ever navigated as an Autistic person. Marriage and parenthood require constant effort and cultivation. The key difference to why the relationship with my wife works and past relationships did not, comes down to the simple yet circular reason that it just works. For reasons I will never truly understand, my wife was never scared off by my unique Autistic self. I would be nowhere without the relationships I have with my family.

Yet, having this fantastic family doesn't translate to me having lots of friends; I don't. It's not because I don't *want* to (although it's not a priority), it's because I'm not that great at making friends and keeping them, as my earlier school stories illustrate. It comes down to acceptance and understanding on both parts; the Autistic friend and the neurotypical friend. It's great if someone wants to be your friend but if you relax into it and be yourself, and then the "friend" doesn't like you when you're being you, that friendship is unsustainable on both ends.

Although all Autistic people have their own personalities, preferences, and differences, the idea that we can't and don't want to form friendships and relationships is wrong. Myth busted.

## MYTH 5:

### AUTISTIC PEOPLE ARE SAVANTS

It's a complete myth that all Autistic people are savants or have savant-like skills. A very successful movie from 1988 had a lot to do with perpetrating this myth due to an Autistic character that could perform complex calculations in the blink of an eye.

There are in fact, a lot of Autistic characters in mainstream movies and TV that really aren't helping this myth. These roles are caricatures—exaggerated characters to catch the audience's attention and intrigue, and so the ratings go up. However, these roles are often played by neurotypical people and they're written by neurotypical writers; they have taken their neurotypical knowledge and a lot of artistic you-know-what, and created highly implausible roles removed from most real lived experiences of Autistic people, certainly all the experiences I have had and know about.

This is not to say there are not Autistic savants or Autistic people with savant-like skills; there are, however, they are rare.[6] This combination of conditions is not stock standard. You can be a math genius or a science whiz, or even a kid doctor whether you're Autistic or neurotypical or have savant syndrome; it happens when it happens. There is no one singular Autistic model.

I know I keep saying it but all Autistic people have their own individual challenges and strengths, IQ levels, and intellectual abilities. You don't become a savant the day you're diagnosed Autistic. Don't believe everything you see on TV in general, let alone relating to autism.

## MYTH 6:

### AUTISTIC PEOPLE ARE VIOLENT

This myth is actually really important to talk about and break down. From my perspective, the news media can portray Autistic people in a very specific way that just isn't appropriate or even fair.

There is absolutely no evidence that Autistic people are more violent than non-Autistic or neurotypical people. In fact, research has shown here in Australia that Autistic people are more likely to be the victims of violence than the perpetrators.[7] I can tell you from my own point of view, certainly watching my son grow up as an Autistic child: Autistic people are almost ripe for the picking in terms of being victims of bullying, manipulation, harassment, and exploitation. So this idea that we're born violent perpetrators is unfair and ridiculous.

It's no different to the neurotypical world. Some people are going to commit crimes, but it doesn't mean just because you're born Autistic, you have a higher propensity for violence or committing crime. It's just plain wrong.

I can tell you that as an Autistic adult, I can look back on my life and remember many scenarios where I've been in overload, in absolute sensory meltdown and this has come across to people as anger or aggression. Autistic meltdowns are manifestations of brain responses triggered by under or overstimulation and various other potential triggers.

> **It is critical to understand that to the untrained eye, an Autistic meltdown (our brain shutting down to recalibrate us internally) can appear as a controllable response or tantrum. It isn't.**

It is an *uncontrollable* response by our brain. If we need to stand up abruptly and brush past you to get away, that's what we do instinctively as a survival response to extreme cognitive overload and sensory issues and environments in a neurotypical world. I'm obviously not saying that means that if I have a meltdown, I can violently attack someone. No, I cannot. Any moments I've had where neurotypical people have considered my reaction as angry, too aggressive or inappropriate, has a caveat that I was not born violent or aggressive, I was born Autistic. And my ability to manage sensory overload is finite.

It's importantly for every single person on the planet to understand that it might appear to manifest as an out-of-control reaction but it's not, not at the soul of it. It is our instinctive survival cells pressing the CTRL+ALT+DEL buttons all at once in order to cope, to survive in an overwhelming world.

In my experience, and watching my son in his experience, I can tell you that Autistic people actually don't stand for bullying and absolutely hate to see it. An Autistic person can often be the first person to call someone out for bullying or malicious aggression. That is a huge upshot of being honest all of the time; it means we see the injustice and will tell people what's going on regardless of the repercussions.

## MYTH 7:

### AUTISM IS A MENTAL ILLNESS

Earlier you heard that autism is not a disease. You can't cure autism. You're born with it. Likewise, autism is not a mental illness. Autism is a neurological developmental difference. That doesn't mean that mental illnesses can't occur in Autistic people because they can and they do at higher levels than neurotypical people. But that's a comorbidity; they co-occur in addition to being Autistic. Having a brain that's wired differently allows you to see and experience the world around you differently to a neurotypical person. So being diagnosed with depression, anxiety, or other mental illnesses is in addition to being Autistic.

I have experienced anxiety for a big part of my life. And I sometimes wonder if all Autistic people are in fact anxious at a level not experienced by neurotypical people and therefore don't need to be diagnosed with anxiety. But I don't believe this to be the case as there is a significant difference between natural levels of anxiety and having a diagnosable form of anxiety. I have two forms by the way, Generalised Anxiety Disorder and Social Anxiety Disorder.

The bottom line is anyone facing the challenges of this busy, stressful neurotypical world may develop depression, anxiety and other mental illnesses but you cannot develop autism. Autism is a neurological developmental difference, not a mental illness.

## MYTH 8:

### ONLY BOYS CAN BE AUTISTIC

Let's blow the myth that only boys can be Autistic right out of the water. As it stands today, boys are approximately three times more likely to be diagnosed Autistic than girls[8] but that does not mean for a second that women and girls aren't diagnosed Autistic on a daily basis. There has long been a traditional disparity and assumption that girls can't be Autistic, which has resulted in discriminatory attitudes when assessing and diagnosing women and girls for autism.

I know of many instances where a young girl or teenager has been misdiagnosed with a condition such as OCD, ADHD, or an eating disorder, only to discover later in life (when they are still feeling broken and disconnected from the world) that in actual fact they were born Autistic. The emotional challenges, fixations and anxieties they had always experienced had been misinterpreted and ultimately misdiagnosed as something other than autism. They had lived years or even decades under a false impression, wondering desperately why nothing seemed to make sense in their world. This is heartbreaking.

Finally research is starting to show that Autistic girls and Autistic women are simply better at camouflaging their true Autistic self and fitting into social situations and expressing themselves in a way that can seem, on the surface, to be neurotypical. They appear to have friends so therefore people say, "...she can't be Autistic." Girls can be much better at group interactions in general.

> **Undiagnosed Autistic girls can appear to fit in socially as the "quiet" or "shy" girl who other girls are drawn to care for because of their nurturing nature.**

It can be much harder to uncover the real Autistic person inside for girls, but they are there. As a result of women and girls having this ability to suppress their Autistic traits (not consciously, more an innate type of masking), in my opinion, this has led to the history of prolonged misdiagnosis for girls and women. Then if they are "lucky" they might get a late diagnosis as opposed to never finding out they're Autistic. There is a gender bias at the core of an autism assessment but also within the wider community. Let me explain.

If I allow myself to interact with others as my true Autistic self I will often be viewed as intense, brooding or different in an interesting way. However, when an Autistic woman drops her mask she is labelled a bitch. So I'm intense yet cool while an Autistic woman is just a rude bitch. This is not acceptable on any level. In my opinion, there is a lost generation of Autistic girls who are now adults coming to a realisation they've been misdiagnosed and I want to acknowledge how draining and damaging it has been for them. Better awareness and information of these circumstances will absolutely help their lives.

Some sources will paint the picture that now more women than men are being diagnosed Autistic. This can make sense on the premise that the ratio of boys to girls being diagnosed is still disproportionate. So more women are going to slip through the net than men, although my story shows it's certainly possible for anyone to slip through.

Autism is not the exclusive property of boys. In fact it never has been. It's just taken time for knowledge and research to catch up. The core contributing factor to misdiagnoses now is a healthcare profession unwilling or unable to embrace that evolving knowledge and research.

# 📢 PLENTY OF FISH IN THE SEA OR QUITE THE CATCH

Have you heard the phrases, "There's plenty of fish in the sea" or, "They're quite the catch"?

So, does this mean that people shouldn't worry about finding someone because at some point they will find someone that's right for them? Further, you will find them by catching them in a relatively barbaric way, you will then starve them of the very environment they need to sustain life, you will wrap them in newspaper, take them home and store them in your freezer until you wish to then cut them open, debone and eat them?

Aren't people looking for someone they can share their life with, not catch, take home and put in the freezer? If you're catching people to be your next partner, I'm calling the police. What? Are you standing on the corner with a little bag? Seriously!

# CHAPTER 4 | AUTISTIC TRAITS

*Everyone should know!*

My book is about cutting through a lot of that medical jargon that often aids and abets people's misconceptions about autism, as contrary as that may sound. In my experience, people are quick to make judgements about someone based on their first impression, no matter how fleeting. I'm asking you to take what I'm about to present here, and keep it in mind next time you're interacting with someone who may not be responding according to your "expectations." I need you to look for the details, the clues, the hints that might just indicate someone is doing the very best they can, yet they are still struggling to conform in the challenging environment that you haven't even noticed.

Below are some Autistic traits in adults that you may never have realised were actually signs of autism. To begin with is a simple list of 20 traits you may not be aware of, to get you thinking about potential reasons behind behaviours you might relate to or have seen in others.

Keep in mind that relating to a few of these traits does not make you Autistic and I am not a healthcare professional, nor is this book a diagnostic tool. However, if you have experienced these traits from childhood or they resonate with you, you may wish to seek an assessment by a healthcare practitioner.

# AUTISTIC TRAITS IN ADULTS AT A GLANCE

→ Feeling uncomfortable, awkward, or anxious around new people and places.

→ Using planned structures, scripts, or conversation templates for making small talk or conversation with others.

→ Aversion to hugging, kissing or shaking hands with people when greeting them.

→ Preferring to wear noise-cancelling headphones or earbuds when you leave the house to drown out all the noises and sensory overload.

→ Noises or sounds seem to become louder when you're tired, stressed, or overstimulated.

→ Easily startled or experience a disproportionate reaction to sudden, loud or unexpected noises.

→ Intolerance to the feeling of certain fabrics or textures.

→ Removing the tags off your clothes and underwear because they drive you crazy and cause sensory overload.

→ Not being able to wear certain types of clothing because it doesn't feel right, or it makes you feel angry or agitated even if it's not uncomfortable.

→ The texture or feel of certain foods makes you gag (e.g. pumpkin).

→ Repelled by certain smells or flavours of food, and just thinking about that food can make you feel sick (e.g. for me, it's peas).

→ Feeling utterly exhausted after leaving your safe place to go shopping, attend appointments, or social situations.

→ Spending more time than necessary in the toilet or bathroom just to escape the world and relax.

→ Preferring to be alone in social gatherings or to stay close to your safe people. You may hang out with your kids instead of mingling.

→ Enjoying people-watching or watching the world go by when at restaurants, cafes, or shops, rather than conversation etc.

→ Always shopping at a specific supermarket, café, or shop because you prefer the comfort of knowing where everything is: parking, items, sections, people.

→ People struggle to connect with you and view you as quirky, odd, or weird.

→ People may seem to laugh more at things you've said or done when you weren't trying to be funny or make them laugh. → *I'm being serious, that wasn't a joke.*

→ You always seem to get into disagreements or arguments with others without intending to or having any idea how it came about or even what it's about.

→ You are told by workmates or reprimanded by your boss for being too blunt or rude, or using an inappropriate tone of voice. Turns out honestly is NOT the best policy.

# UNDERSTANDING AUTISTIC TRAITS

Next, I want to slow it down and delve deeper into some of the foundational categories of Autistic behaviour that are often true for many Autistic children and adults but not necessarily everyone. Some Autistic people will lean more heavily on certain behaviours for comfort and support than others; every Autistic person is different.

If everyone can learn to recognise these signs and behaviours more often (in yourself or a loved one) then the future will have more compassion and acceptance than I see and experience now, which is my ultimate goal. I must create a brighter, more hopeful future for my sons.

## ROUTINES

Okay, the first trait to recognise is routines. Autistic people, including me, rely heavily on specific daily routines and rituals. For the most part, routines keep us balanced and regulated in a world designed to put us off balance, designed to deregulate us. Daily routines aren't there just to look quirky or weird or come across as boring to the outsider. Routines are actually crucial to our mental health. When our world is already upside down from being an Autistic person in a neurotypical world, finding some sort of regularity, structure and predictability helps give us peace.

I understand for parents of Autistic kids or even partners and family members, it can seem like groundhog day, but it's not to the Autistic person. There's very real and genuine importance and value in these routines, far more than any neurotypical person would ever see or understand; but that's okay, after all, how could you know if you've never had it explained to you before? **If you understand the importance of routine and you accept it, and allow it, and *embrace* it, it will make such a difference in an Autistic person's life.** The regulation it provides us is mutually beneficial.

Routines help me survive and recover from day-to-day life so I can continue to live on this neurotypical planet. It sounds dramatic, but frankly for me (and I can't speak on behalf of anyone else), I can tell you right now, without understanding and acceptance, every day is really tiring. I don't mean that to garner sympathy—you know me better than that by now—it's just the truth.

Now don't lock these in for all eternity, but some examples of Autistic routines you might have seen but not recognised for what they are: it might be a rigid order to daily tasks, set times for activities, reliance on quiet time and, in my case, a nap every day. Seriously, I have a routine for everything, including how I shower, eat, sleep, relax (although I'm not entirely sure I relax in the classic neurotypical sense) and how I create content.

For me, when I go to the shops, I expect to buy specific brands, specific products, specific types of bread and milk, while relying on the shop layout never changing. If I can't buy what I need there, if the products aren't available—even a single item—

that's a big deal for me. I know people do get a bit annoyed with that in general but what I mean is I will stop shopping, I will put everything back where it belongs on the shelf, and I will go to another shop and hope the item (and all the other items) are there. That change in expectation and routine is a massive issue for me.

In fact, if any of my plans or predicted events change at the last minute or have to be altered, it renders me virtually useless on the premise that I struggle to be flexible and outright reject the idea. If I was planning on doing something and something changed at the last minute and I've got to do that something at a different time, you can get stuffed. I'm not doing it at a different time. I was going to do it at a particular time, that's how I planned it, mentally prepared for it and it can only operate under those planned parameters or not at all.

So, change in routine is not good. Another example would be if I was in a typical workplace (I'm not anymore, but let's say I were), and the way I did things at work had to change suddenly. You might think, *Well, who cares that your desk was moved? Or your job or hours have changed? It happens!*

Well, as an Autistic person that would legitimately shake me to my foundations, and seriously impact me for a seemingly disproportionate amount of time. I know it sounds like a tantrum, but it's not. It relates to the consequences of having to relinquish control over something that we desperately need control over to stay regulated. The fallout can lead to Autistic meltdown, which you'll learn about shortly.

## STIMMING

Another Autistic trait you should definitely get to know is stimming, more formally referred to as self-stimulatory behaviour, which falls under the category of "restricted or repetitive behaviours." Stimming is one of the most effective methods (it's free and easy) that Autistic people turn to, to calm themselves down, self soothe and regulate themselves when their brain is heading towards some form of overload (including sensory overload).

Some people say that everyone, even neurotypical people, stim. I get where they're coming from, because stimming is what we call "self-stimulation" from an Autistic point of view. Neurotypical people might turn to taking a break, having a cup of tea or coffee, or taking a nap whenever they feel overloaded or tired.

When an Autistic person is overwhelmed, we have passed the threshold of our ability to deal with what's going on around us, and in order to avoid meltdown we start physically doing specific actions to alleviate the intensity we are feeling in that moment.

I stim a lot and many times I don't even know I'm doing it. But clearly (if you know to look), it's a sign to other people that I am becoming deregulated and I'm doing my best to regulate, soothe and calm myself down. For some reason I move my fingers a lot, I like to play with my fingers, touch my fingers. I like to get my thumb or a finger and kind of do laps. I also like to use my thumbs and my fingers on my fingers, tracing shapes, or letters, or numbers.

Outwardly what I'm doing might appear arbitrary, but the polar opposite is true. I'm actually writing words that I'm thinking in my head on my fingers. I'm not doing it for fun; I'm doing it because the repetitive thought and motion is relaxing. I play with my hair a lot too; I like to grab little bits of hair in the corner of my skull and kind of pull them to feel the tension on my scalp. I know that sounds bizarre and strange, but it brings me back to the moment, back into myself and the sensory overload that caused me to stim fades to a manageable level.

I can also be quite fidgety or restless. I find it hard to sit still and hard to feel relaxed in what *Theoretically.* would be considered comfortable positions for neurotypical people, like sitting around a table. I almost always prefer standing to sitting, which constantly leads people to ask me, "Why are you standing?" To which I could justifiably reply, "Why are you sitting?"

To add real life context to the importance of understanding why Autistic people stim, let's say you and I are in a conversation together and you see me start to stim. I'm trying to stay regulated while I am in a challenging social environment as well as trying to process what you're saying. There's a lot going on so I start stimming. I might also be avoiding eye contact as this helps to minimise my sensory overload when communicating (I'll expand on this later if you promise not to judge when I look the other way.)

**From my point of view, in order to engage with you, I am stimming and avoiding eye contact so I can process what you're saying. I am trying to hear you and respect you.**

Yet from your point of view, I'm not looking you in the eye and I appear to just be rudely fidgeting and not even paying attention. You can imagine how people react to that interaction, thinking I constantly disrespect them in conversations when actually I'm doing both those things to engage with them as much as possible! Until we can get more awareness out there, it's a lose/lose situation that follows me home mentally every day.

By the way, unless you're a pirate, the expression, "Look me in the eye" is moot. You want me to look you in the eye? Which one? It takes more effort to focus on one eye. I'm getting dizzy just thinking about it.

There is a final irony about stimming I'd like to finish on. What triggers my Autistic son (we'll get to triggers soon so stay tuned, still heaps of solid gold, grade A content to come), doesn't trigger me and what triggers me, doesn't trigger him. This presents a pretty unique real-life scenario where learning to become an Autistic father to an Autistic son meant I faced new challenges, triggers and overwhelm, to which I started stimming in the quirky ways that I do.

For me, this plays out when I can't stop saying obscure catch-phrases from movies or TV shows or ads over and over again (this is referred to as echolalia). Or I use weird voices, some people might call them annoying; I just think they're funny and I can't stop. I won't stop. This is the form of stimming that I rely on to help me become a better dad by grounding me and bringing me back, but it actually triggers and sets off my Autistic son.

> How can you parent as an Autistic dad, if your methods of soothing yourself and calming yourself down, actually trigger the Autistic son you're looking after who is, in fact, triggering you, causing you to stim in the first place, thereby causing him to trigger?

You see what's happening? While I'm trying to care for him and look after him, he'll do things naturally that raise my level of anxiety. Of course he does, he's an Autistic kid; I totally 100% get it.

However, my son has very little idea of danger. He thinks it's okay to jump from the top of the stairs to the bottom of the stairs. And it is okay if no one minds that he could fall onto the concrete slab breaking both legs, it's perfectly fine. But my anxiety goes up and then I start to get a little bit agitated. I start stimming, this starts triggering him, that starts triggering me, I do my things to help my trigger, that triggers him more. Next thing you know, fire and gasoline.

This is tiring, awkward, challenging and true, part of my warts-and-all account of real life living as an Autistic father to an Autistic son and I know I'm not the only one in this situation. Fortunately, I understand what's going on and it allows my wife and I to navigate it together, as a team fully aware of everybody's strengths and weaknesses.

So now, hopefully you can see the tip of the iceberg that represents the Autistic need for stimming. Recognise it, accept it and embrace it. Go the stim.

## FAST TALKING

Fast talking is another Autistic trait and one that especially applies to me. I talk fast all the time and from my point of view, it's because my brain is going at such a speed of thoughts that I don't want you to miss out. I really want you to hear everything that I'm thinking and to do that I've got to catch up on everything waiting to be said yet I never can catch up, but that doesn't mean I'll stop trying, it's pre-programmed.

So I'm compelled to talk really fast and not stop, no breaths, nothing. And I know it comes across a bit manic, but it's not. I'm not manic, I'm Autistic and my brain's going so fast and I can't stop and the more excited I get, the faster I go.

If I don't get that thought out, the next thought has already taken over and I'll forget the previous one which is really frustrating because in my mind, it's imperative to the topic at hand so I'm often butting in and interrupting. One way or another, I just need to share this stuff before it's gone. I don't realise that in doing so, I'm breaching those rules of communication in the neurotypical world. There's no intention from me to do that, it's simply that something is so amazing that I want to share it with you.

Even though I'm firing off thoughts and words at a seemingly inexhaustible speed, you'd be surprised to know how much I am concentrating on trying to get the words out clearly, making sure that you can understand my full meaning.

You'll recall from earlier my practice of talking in what I consider to be slow motion. Thankfully radio and podcasts mean you can't see me as my mouth over pronounces and elongates the syllables in every word; it slows me down so I sound at my neurotypical, communicating best! It's totally ridiculous and exhausting but an Autistic person's brain is different, and they may speak passionately, or rant or butt in, or might not stop talking because it's coming from a brain that's simply wired differently in the way that it communicates and receives information.

I have spent years honing this particular skill of masking my natural speed, yet if that's what I have to do to get my message out there, I will. Tune in and listen for yourself!

## FIXATION

This is a really good trait to point out and clear up: intense fixation. When you think I'm zoning out, when you think I'm daydreaming, off with the fairies or the lights are on but nobody's home, that is not what's happening. No, my lights never turn off champ and I'm always home. Home is my safe place.

But it's a busy time up there. Sometimes I have to ask my Autistic son the same question 20 times, it feels like I can't reach him. The bottom line is, there's a difference between a neurotypical person zoning out and a neurodivergent person "zoning out"; my son is not really zoning out at all. He's regulating himself through fixating on a particular passion of his. You may call it fixation, but for me it's more of a logical action.

For example, I will drop everything to fix something in the house immediately, even if it's not a priority to the family. Nothing and no one can reach me; I must complete the task of resolving the situation. In my experience, Autistic people tend to have an intense focus or fixation on particular passions or special interests to the exclusion of all else, immersing in the task is extremely calming and reassuring. It can also be challenging to maintain attention and stay present when the topic has no interest, appeal or direct relevance to me.

## INTENSE INTERESTS AND PASSIONS

I have never been comfortable with the term "special interests." In my view, the use of the word "special" is an insult. Like anyone with a disability, we all have individual needs, different needs. You are not a parent of a "special needs" kid. You're the parent of an Autistic child, who happens to have some different needs. My different brain doesn't make me special; it makes me different.

To be clear, I believe all parents, carers and partners of Autistic people use the word "special" in good faith. I am not blaming you, but I am calling on you to make a change for the better. Many medical terms have changed over time due to evolving standards, knowledge, and preferences. This is one of those terms. In saying that, I will refer to these as intense interests, special interests or passions going forward to avoid alienating anyone.

Intense interests and passion for particular subjects can play an enormous role in the life of an Autistic person. The particular interest can range from the normal to the unusual but the key is **there's an intensity to that level of interest that may seem disproportionate to a neurotypical person.** We have a hunger to know and learn everything about our specific interests.

It is a mistake to think our interests and passions are just hobbies we dabble in when we find some spare time. I'm not even sure if Autistic people have hobbies. I certainly do not. Why would I? I struggle to find enough time for my interests and passions. Our interests are like oxygen to an Autistic person; our lifeblood that we must live and breathe as often as possible. I would do mine all day and all night to the exclusion of all else if I could.

Conversely, if we are starved of enough time to spend on our interests, it can feel like a life-or-death situation. I know it's not, but inside us there's nothing more important, it lights the world up—a world that can otherwise get in the way of exploring our interests and passions.

> One of the most important pieces of advice I can give parents or carers of Autistic kids is once you find what they're passionate about, let them live it, and then use that to open up the rest of the world to them.

My personal background shows how this can work. I've had a successful career in radio, broadcasting, and communications but there's a specific reason for that. My high-level skills came about because they are inherently part of my interests, my lifelong passions. I started working in community radio when I was 12 years old and commercial radio at 17. Being in radio, doing radio shows, performing, entertaining and learning to push the right buttons from when you're 12 means you're going to develop some high-level skills.

For years now people have said to me, "Hang on, how can you be Autistic? You work in commercial radio." And I can understand it can be a little bit confusing to the uninitiated—I do podcasts, I have a YouTube channel, I present keynote speeches in front of thousands of people, I act, I perform. But these are my interests and my passions that allow me to be me while living out my passion.

It's also important to point out that when I make content (videos and podcasts) there's no one else around and even when I'm speaking in person, it's one-way communication. I'm the speaker and you are the audience. Performing and interacting with others are not the same thing. I'd be happy to perform on stage to hundreds of thousands of people, no worries, but put me in a room with a few people and I'm in hell.

From a very young age I found myself entertaining people and getting a crowd. Looking back, I guess I found acceptance and validation in those audiences, in the laughs and pats on the back. My ability to act, host, perform, and create content has come from years and years of doing what is nothing more than my passion, my intense interest that I want to do all day every day. From literally a toddler right through to being a fully grown man I've honed those skills. It's not rocket science; the more you do things, the better you get.

Allegedly.

If not for my intense interest and passions I would not have the high-level specialty skills I now possess in content creation. Virtually all other areas of my life do not come naturally to me. While the expression, "Jack of all trades, master of none" is a light-hearted neurotypical phrase, it underscores the opposite scenario well for Autistic people. Unlike neurotypical "Jack" who knows a little bit about everything but masters none of them, Autistic people can take an intense interest in a single subject and continue to study that particular interest throughout their life.

These intense interests and passions are a huge Autistic strength that can often be used to everyone's benefit, just as mine have been for my career. It improves our quality of life and we are an untapped supplier in terms of bringing that knowledge into the workforce. Neurodiversity in the workplace is, in my view, one of the greatest untapped resources on earth.

## SOCIAL AND COMMUNICATION CHALLENGES

This is a really big trait to be aware of and show compassion for. Interaction, communication and the social side of normal daily life with neurotypical, non-Autistic people is one of the most challenging and tiring aspects in an Autistic person's day. Our brains as Autistic people are wired differently; we see, feel and experience the world differently. We can't be altered, we can't "not be like that." We can't not be Autistic; there's no on/off switch; we can't leave our brain behind.

Most days I get to stand in a room in my house talking to myself, hoping someone will see it. I sound like I'm talking to you but it's really me talking into a smart phone. There's nothing social about it.

So in real life, social interactions don't go so well. I didn't understand as much when I was in school, but I know I can come across as rude or arrogant, or the opposite demeanour of appearing shy or quiet; disinterested is another look I have. And it is these reactions, or at least my perception of them, that illustrate the war going on inside as I struggle with an inability to feel comfortable in social situations.

When interacting with people I can take a long time to warm up to them, and in between entering and warming up I can come across as everything I said above. Just know that is not what I am trying to convey. I am actually just distressed, deregulated or challenged by the experience. Once I've warmed up though, look out! I am as close to the unmasked, authentic Orion as most will ever get to see! But getting to that point is the hard part and almost never happens.

Interaction for Autistic people involves a lot of masking (stay tuned for that one). In effect this means we are trying to come across neurotypical and suppress our natural Autistic selves. For example, I would never ask someone a small-talk question such as, "What's the weather like?" I give no thought whatsoever to these kinds of generic questions and I hate answering them.

If you ask me, "How was the drive?" internally the question staggers me, because I have absolutely no investment in how my drive was, who cares? I got in a car, I drove here, I got out. Why are you making me think about something so incredibly pointless and boring? Those thoughts are in my brain but I try to suppress them in order to answer the question.

> **Most of the time I am masking when in a social situation; ironically I still manage to get it wrong most of the time. I'm just trying to act like some sort of agreeable neurotypical person.**

Another trait that can create friction is that I tend to only want to talk about something I'm interested in. You might ask me a question and I'll get rolling and I won't know when to stop. The thought of stopping so you can say something (to which I won't know what to say) makes me anxious so I keep talking!

I also really struggle to know when people are no longer interested in what I'm saying. Just ask anyone who has ever phoned me or asked me a question, ever. A hairdresser once asked me how I was and I went on to speak about the eventual death of the sun for 20 minutes. I compared my feelings to the inner collapse of the sun. Don't get me started on the fact that some people don't know that our sun is a star that will eventually die.

Knowing when and how to end conversations is really tricky, especially on the phone. I'll never understand how to get to the end or how to move on or how to close it, I just don't understand the tones and hints that say the other person is preparing to wrap it up. I'm just so bad at that stuff which explains why I've spent my entire life, my career talking to myself on radio, podcasts, and videos!

# HYPERSENSITIVITY

Hypersensitivity is another important Autistic trait to know, look out for and show understanding for. I can be hypersensitive to things like smells and sounds. Smells can actually really trigger me, for example if I'm in my house and I smell an unusual, odd smell, I'll immediately demand from my wife and kids, "What's that horrible smell?!"

My wife often replies that she doesn't smell anything and like a bloodhound, I am insistent that it's coming from somewhere and keep looking until I can find the smell, identify the smell and eradicate the smell. Until this happens, the situation is an open crime scene. My wife says my hearing and sense of smell is kind of superhero-like. Weird smells and unexpected noises can really shake me to the core.

After a loud, unexpected noise, some people would remark, "Gee, that was a bit loud," but for me, I'm telling you, that noise shocked the bejesus out of me. It doesn't scare me conventionally but I'm so hypersensitive to sounds and smells that my nervous system has a huge reaction and I can't settle down for ages. It's a massive challenge for me and it's a trait that you will find some Autistic people absolutely suffer from or at least experience as a challenge especially when they do head out into the world.

Recognising these sensory triggers in Autistic people can help you to be a little bit more protective and caring and understanding, around not only yourself and your family, but the Autistic person in your life.

## 📢 TWO BIRDS, ONE STONE

People still use the phrase, "You can kill two birds with one stone". What are you? An animal serial killer? "Hey look, there's a stone, that's a good stone, that's a bird–killing stone that one."

"Where are you off to mate?"

"I'm off to kill some birds."

"Make sure you kill two! Do you have a stone?"

"Yeah I've got a good stone!"

# CHAPTER 5

# LESS-**KNO**WN AUTISTIC TRAITS

*But just as important.*

Chapter 4 talked you through some of the most common Autistic traits but I must go deeper than that in the name of every struggle and misconstrued moment I have battled through over decades.

I want you and the wider community to recognise and understand as many layers to autism (and neurodivergence) as possible, so these insights become the beginning of huge positive change for my son, my family and anyone from any part of the world looking to strengthen their relationships and compassion within the autism community.

These frequently overlooked features include speech, communication, and perception-related traits, as well as something I absolutely experience on a daily basis, face blindness (technically called prosopagnosia). I'll also expand on fearlessness, connection to the natural world, motor skill challenges and gastrointestinal problems. As always, this is not intended to be a diagnostic tool. It is simply a further discussion of autism traits seen through the lens of my lived experiences.

# NO-FILTER COMMUNICATION

An important lesser-known Autistic trait that you should know is no-filter communication. Take me for example, as an Autistic person I tend to say exactly what I'm thinking, say exactly what I believe, and say exactly what I mean. In no way does it even occur to me to repackage my thoughts and feelings. I'm just honestly communicating them to you and I would assume that's how everyone wants to be communicated to, in an honest, open fashion...

However, the Autistic trait of no-filter communication can really create barriers when communicating with neurotypical people, who are predisposed to communicating in a way where they don't say *exactly* what they mean, or necessarily mean what they say. They often speak in layers of etiquette and propriety out of conditioning or guilt or fear of offending.

Straight up, honest and literal is exactly how my Autistic brain not only communicates but also receives information. This is actually my strong suit, communication at its best. Saying what you mean, meaning what you say, explicit in your communication. Some people might call it black and white, with no grey area, open and honest. Others refer to it as concrete thinking. However you describe it, that's my way of communicating which happens to be the opposite to the majority of the world's style of communicating.

> **A result of the conventional not-saying-what-you-mean thing is making an Autistic no-filter response appear as rude, arrogant, or even brutal when seen through the eyes of a neurotypical person.**

From my point of view though, I'm just communicating exactly what I think based on your question. I'm giving you the information you literally asked for! I'm not trying to filter or not filter because in my mind it doesn't occur to me that filtering is required when someone's asked me a question and I'm giving them my answer. For me, honesty is kindness, whereas for neurotypical people, not being honest is closer to their idea of kindness.

I'm putting information out there. I'm not receiving it on your behalf, that's your job. Although it may come across like I'm intentionally not filtering my words, objectively I'm in no way trying to be brutal or rude, but just trying to communicate to you what I think, which can be a black-and-white, honest, open, straightforward answer, response or contribution to the conversation.

For me as an Autistic person, I absolutely struggle to dissect the meaning behind your words if in fact, the words that you're conveying actually contradict the real meaning of what you're trying to tell me. At one end of this navigational nightmare is the reality that some neurotypical people intentionally say the opposite of what they actually want or mean.

At the other end is a simple difference of navigational styles. For example, when I decide to go to bed and my wife is still watching TV, I often say, "I'm going to bed, do you want me to leave the TV on?"

To which my wife often replies, "I've got to go to bed too." I didn't hear her say whether to leave it on or turn it off, so I will ask again and again until I get the answer I require to my question. Saying, "I've got to go to bed too," doesn't tell me when you will actually go to bed and if you still want the TV left on, but it clearly does to my wife.

I'm not trying to undo centuries of conversational conditioning for neurotypical people, but am simply trying to highlight a neurological trait that many Autistic people have in order for everyone to appreciate the good intentions behind open and honest communication, with no filter, in every setting.

## TALKING VOLUME AND PACE

In general terms, Autistic people can struggle to realise that they may be talking at a louder level than is appropriate or their talking pace may not suit the situation. As an Autistic person with an Autistic son, I can tell you (putting me aside for a second), it is not just a daily factor it's a minute-by-minute factor.

My wife and I are almost constantly reminding him that he's talking loudly. We use a constructive, practical way to talk about it, referring to his vocal chords as his "workers" that like to stay in the green zone. So when our son talks in the red zone, we say, "Hey, little buddy, your workers are in the red zone. You're talking a little bit loudly and you're hurting your workers. You want to get down to the green zone."

This helps him create awareness of something tangible, to feel where his voice is originating rather than just saying, "Your voice is too loud," when voice and volume for most people is an unconscious creation.

Like my son, I get feedback like this a lot, "You're talking too loudly Orion. Can you keep your voice down a little? Can you talk a bit softer? Don't yell Orion." I'm surprised each time, "Hang on, I'm not even close to yelling. I'm sorry, I didn't realise I was talking loudly... Really, I'm talking loudly?" There's no insight I can draw upon. I legitimately and genuinely don't have the inkling that in that moment I'm talking at a level and volume that's inappropriate for the situation. It just doesn't occur to me.

And remember as a person with an Autistic brain, I am 100% processing, perceiving, and experiencing the world in a completely different way through a completely different brain. If I'm experiencing, processing, perceiving the world differently, how can I be expected to reciprocate it all back in the same way as a neurotypical person experiences the world? I cannot.

As I've already revealed, I have learnt (over many long, arduous years of trying) to slow down my style of talking,

*Bloody rhetorical question got me again, and it's my own words.*

constantly telling myself to talk "quietly" and almost exaggerate my words which equates to a version of "normal" that works in media communication.

The takeaway from this particular lesser-known trait about volume and pace of talking is remembering where it's coming from. It's coming from an Autistic brain which is different. The most important thing is to acknowledge that and listen with sensitivity when we may talk fast and passionately and won't know when to stop. It's all coming from a brain that's wired differently in the way it communicates and receives information.

# PROSOPAGNOSIA (FACE BLINDNESS)

In essence, prosopagnosia is where a person struggles to recognise and identify the face of a person they know. The likelihood of experiencing face blindness is higher for Autistic people than the general population.[9]

Face blindness most often occurs for me in out-of-context situations. For example, let's say I'm out shopping or down the street in a public place, and someone just comes up to me, unsolicited and says straight away, "Hello Orion, how are you? What's been happening?"

Now, I can see they obviously know me and we should know each other. But there are a few potential reasons for me not being able to respond as they expect. It can be because I just wasn't prepared to suddenly see, meet or catch up with person A or person B, particularly in a different setting to how we know each other, and undoubtedly I wasn't thinking about them one way or another.

While I'm still struggling to work out who this person is, they have already surged ahead with questions and conversation. I'm trying to play along but really, I'm doing a very bad job of it because the whole time I'm pushing myself, pushing my brain: *Who is this person? What's their name for goodness sake? You have to know Orion, come on! They're talking to you like you're friends.* The whole time, my brain is scrambling trying to place them but I can't.

A common experience is when I've encountered work colleagues in non-workplace environments; it's often just too out-of-context for me to connect the dots quickly enough. It's situations where I'm completely unprepared for meeting someone unexpectedly, or if I'm very focused on something else or overwhelmed by what I'm already doing. This might include the grocery shopping, down the street where there's lots of stimulation already, in the park with my kids, or anywhere I am out of my comfort zone and it takes a lot of effort to simply be there. Many times, these encounters get very awkward and I look like an idiot, but it's a legitimate struggle.

Some Autistic people experience face blindness constantly, as in, they have a condition where they cannot recognise people from looking at their face. So, the takeaway for neurotypical parents, carers, friends and family of Autistic people is we are not in any way trying to be rude or obstructive. It's legitimately our brain ticking over in a situation where we just can't place a face; for one reason or another there's a blockage. I know it can become not only rude, but also awkward and uncomfortable.

My advice is to be on the front foot when you are out with someone who you know is Autistic. This means if you see someone familiar coming towards you, help out the Autistic person in your life by getting in first. Be proactive and if there's time use direct, explicit language such as:

> Hey, look! It's Karen from my work, you met her at the Christmas party.

Or if there is no time to forewarn them, you can still add detail in your greeting that will help your Autistic companion.

> Hi, Karen, how are you going? Do you remember Orion from the Christmas party?

Spell out whatever context applies to help the Autistic person place the face. (Now that's an idea for a game show, "Welcome to Place the Face, and here's your face blind host Orion Kelly!"). If you are the person who is approaching someone you know to be Autistic and they look at you a bit lost, show some intuition by giving them a lead-in to what your connection is:

> Hi Orion, it's Jenny from your son's day care, I haven't seen you out and about for a while, have you been busy making more videos?

Either way, just understand and accept that some Autistic people may have the challenge of face blindness.

# FEARLESSNESS

If you have an Autistic person in your life, or you're Autistic, the tendency for fearlessness is something you probably know well. Yet some people reading this might also think, *Hang on, it doesn't make sense, you always talk about being anxious not fearless.* And yes, as a comorbidity sure, I have anxiety. There are Autistic people who have comorbidities of all kinds, but there's a difference between having anxiety and experiencing moments of fearlessness. Let's talk about it.

Now, you may have an Autistic friend or a family member who at some point has wandered off. In the neurotypical sense, wandering really implies a gentle meandering to relax or taking a stroll. In the Autistic sense, wandering is more like a broad term that's akin to suddenly running away, a sudden change of mind, or just ending up somewhere you didn't think you would go. For example, if an Autistic child was at the beach and then out of nowhere, they just started sprinting full pelt in the opposite direction or darting towards the ocean, that would be classed as Autistic wandering.

Part of this fearlessness in Autistic people is this impulse to act now and think later. Often, we don't really consider the consequences of the action. We just want to do it impulsively and so we do it.

> **Autistic people can, from time to time, put themselves in danger due to a possible lack of perception that a danger exists, even as we are moving towards it.**

I also think that fearlessness is connected to an Autistic person's lack of impulse control or a challenge to control impulses. Every Autistic person is different, but in general terms, some strong impulses may be connected to regulation, sensory input and processing. For example, I may reach out to touch the material of someone's clothing without asking them, or seek a sensory input without considering the implications or proximity of others.

I can't speak on behalf of every Autistic person but from my point of view, I'm impulsive. I struggle to control my impulses. I feel like I'm impulsive by nature. You might call it spontaneous, but for me it's completely different. I rely on daily plans and routines to maintain peace of mind, in a constantly changing world. Whereas, if my wife asks me to get milk and bread from the shops I will often return with two bags of less-than-healthy snacks I just had to have.

As an Autistic adult with a neurotypical wife I find that my impulsive nature can be a blessing and a curse. The way an impulsive nature can manifest in an Autistic person can be quite attractive to potential friends and partners. You can appear carefree and childlike in a good way. Conversely, I may experience certain impulses that are out of context or not in step with the wants and needs of others.

# CONNECTION TO THE NATURAL WORLD

A connection to the outdoors, animals, the environment, nature and the planet is a trait of many Autistic people and it's not hard to understand why. Animals are pretty easy to connect with, are not hard to read or interpret, don't place unrealistic expectations on you, they love you unconditionally and they're an open book. So you can see why Autistic people in general have a real connection to animals. You know where you stand and you can just be yourself.

So if you have an Autistic person in your life don't shy away from that. Embrace that because it's beneficial for everyone. I've always found peace outdoors, escaping to the environment I've loved since childhood: getting outside, playing some sport, going for bush walks, riding my bike, the calming nature of the coast, hearing and feeling nature—it just brings me back to a calm centre of everything.

My son's connection to animals and the environment is in that wild, adventurous, dreaming stage where he absolutely wants to be a zoologist. He thinks he will be the next Steve Irwin, travelling to exotic places and hanging out with animals the whole time. Beautiful and dangerous.

It's all about getting outside and just having fun, feeling the air, feeling the environment, feeling the sun, just whatever you want to do, just do stuff outside. You don't have to do a workout routine, just get out there and enjoy yourself. The connection to the natural world is a balm to Autistic burnout and overload and just general everyday wellbeing.

# MOTOR SKILL CHALLENGES

Motor skills, or more appropriately motor skill *challenges*, can be broken down into subcategories of fine motor skills (using finer muscles such as in hands and fingers) and gross motor skills (general balance and coordination). To think of all those times I've been called "unco" (short for uncoordinated) or clumsy! Well, I'm not. I'm Autistic, it's a trait: let's discuss.

We are now beginning to better understand why Autistic people experience motor skill challenges with better insights into the differences in brain processing. For example, it's been found that Autistic children may have a harder time catching a ball than non-Autistic kids.[10]

One of the possible causes that has been offered is that firstly, Autistic kids seem to find it harder to predict the ball's trajectory. Further, Autistic kids seem to speed up the velocity of their hands as the ball approaches, basically launching their hands at the ball instead of slowing their hands down in the vicinity of the predicted trajectory.

As you can imagine, trying to catch a ball by launching your hands at it right before it arrives creates more of a collision; the ball's going to hit your fingers or hands and bounce away. Even today, I have to tell myself to wait for the ball slowly and resist reaching out for it too soon. It's something that needs constant thoughts attached to the process whereas other kids naturally just know, and eventually give it little conscious thought at all as they throw, catch, run, laugh and fool around all at once.

Looking back, I always struggled with consistency in sport. Take cricket for example, one day I might bowl the ball beautifully and maybe get the batsman out, while other times I'll bowl wides and barely even make it onto the cricket pitch. Or I might be batting one day and all I do is swing and miss until I get bowled out, only to find in the next innings my bat connects with every ball and I keep hitting it to the boundary for fours and sixes. My ability was never consistent.

In hindsight, I think it came down to focus and concentration. It's a different level of focus and concentration for an Autistic person to coordinate all the elements and potentially rise to the professional skill level of non-Autistic people. In essence, high-level athletic skill requires an Autistic person to hack their brain and suppress natural instincts, at every moment of every game.

Balance, slower reaction times and movements to music are other areas of coordination that can be challenging for Autistic kids. Learning to ride a bike can take years longer, and for some it might not happen at all. Our Autistic son still prefers scooters to bikes, in large part due to the challenges of balance and coordination.

You know that beat you learn in school or on TV to clap your hands and tap your feet simultaneously? Well, I can't really do those two things at once; it's disjointed, it's lagging, I'm out of beat. Learning to play the drums would be the equivalent of me successfully surviving on Mars with zero support or infrastructure.

Fine motor skills such as tying up shoelaces are a challenge for me to this day. I've never been able to master it. For years I've just pulled them tight so the shoe stays on and the ends just dangle around. Most days I take them off even when I'm working in the studio. While on the subject, the perception of right and left shoes is ridiculously challenging for me. When I help my kids put their shoes on I have to use specific hacks or tricks in my mind to identify which shoe goes on which foot. I can't just look at them and think that's the left shoe. And a lot of times after arriving at school, teachers will say to one of my sons, "Hang on. Your shoes are on the wrong foot. Who put your shoes on today?" And they answer, "Daddy did!" Snitches get stitches boys.

Relax, I'm joking. Though can I just point out that premise is wrong? If you snitch, the punishment isn't stitches, they're the treatment for the punishment. You get attacked and potentially acquire a nasty abrasion, which may require medical treatment, including stitches. Snitches get stitches is just plain wrong.

## GASTROINTESTINAL PROBLEMS

This lesser-known Autistic trait is really interesting and may surprise some as it's not as widely recognised as other traits however, I have first-hand experience with this trait and so does my Autistic son.

I don't believe I've ever had a day without experiencing some level of gastrointestinal discomfort. I have a theory that given the brain can impact the gut and cause various conditions or ailments, an Autistic brain surely must interact and impact the gut of an Autistic person differently to a neurotypical person.

**Could the Autistic brain be behind an increased likelihood of gastrointestinal problems experienced by Autistic people?**

There is ongoing debate amongst researchers, academics, professionals and practitioners about the actual cause or medical link between gastrointestinal problems and autism. I think we have to weigh up a few things in combination with each other. I can feel abdominal discomfort for many reasons, be that eating the wrong foods, stress, anxiety, IBS or too much dairy.

Nowadays I try to follow the FODMAP diet to minimise my chances of intestinal pain. It really works for me and I can tell the difference when I stray from it, by having too much dairy for example. From my point of view, it's a combination of factors when felt through an Autistic brain and body. The problem could be IBS, it could be stress, it could be anxiety. But the sheer nature of my Autistic brain and the way it impacts my makeup, my biology, and the way my body interacts with the world means I'm convinced there's a connection between autism and gastrointestinal problems.

I'm not saying it's *just* being Autistic but the research is showing us statistics that strongly suggest a connection is there.[11] Considering being Autistic also lends itself to other factors like stress and anxiety, no matter which angle you look at it, it all seems to come together and connect.

These lesser-known traits are by no means the cherry on top of genuine understanding and appreciation. They are the structure on top of the slab we laid in previous chapters. Without a working knowledge of the off-broadway traits there is no real understanding, acceptance and appreciation of Autistic people.

## 📢 WE GET ON LIKE A HOUSE ON FIRE

Why do people say, "We get on like a house on fire"? What?! So if a house is on fire, that means the house, that's usually safe, where families live and keep their belongings, precious things, memories, material things, whatever, is now burning down. This house is being destroyed in one of the most violent, dangerous ways possible. It's hot, it's deadly, it's smokey, everything is being destroyed. You get kicked out of your house, you might never get your house back, people could be injured, people could be killed.

This is not something I would say: "You know me and Pete? We get on like the worst day of someone's life, our friendship is dangerous and toxic."

# CHAPTER 6

# AUTISM AND ANXIETY

The connection!

A re Autistic people anxious because they are Autistic or because they have a diagnosable form of anxiety? Or can it be both? I want to explore the connection between autism and having a diagnosed form of anxiety as a co-occurring condition. Understanding how autism and anxiety are related is really important, considering how much trickier and more confronting life as an Autistic person with co-occurring conditions can be.

Being an Autistic person in a neurotypical world isn't a walk in the park at the best of times (though I would need to know more about the park, including the parking layout and toilet facilities) so living with other co-occurring conditions further complicates the challenges of walking in the park. Wait, why am I still in the park? Unless I designed the park and am able to close it to all others while I use it, you can shove your precious walk.

This section is all about giving you helpful insights and understanding into what I consider to be the top forms of diagnosed anxiety conditions experienced by Autistic people. Now admittedly, statistics around autism and anxiety can vary depending on which study you choose to look at, but all the research I have read shows a significant percentage of Autistic people have comorbidities such as diagnosed anxiety, depression or OCD for example.[12]

The notion that anxiety is tied up with an autism diagnosis is wrong. Although the signs of autism and anxiety can appear similar, they are in fact separate conditions that can co-occur. In my case, I am Autistic and have two co-occurring conditions, social anxiety disorder and generalised anxiety disorder.

> **It is crucial to acknowledge autism is a neurological developmental disability, while anxiety is a mental health condition.**

They are not the same diagnosis. I can take medications for my clinical anxiety, whereas autism is not a medically treated illness, it is simply a neurological difference, a neurodivergence.

# SOCIAL ANXIETY DISORDER

Let's look at social anxiety disorder, my first co-occurring condition. In general terms, social anxiety disorder is a persistent fear of social situations, and the fear or anxiety is out of proportion to the actual threat posed by the social situation. In my experience this manifests in an overwhelming sense of solely bad things happening in any social situation, regardless of the context. So it's not just about embarrassment, although it's often the end result of things going bad for me. In fact, I'd go further and say self-hate and self-loathing may be a more predictable result from social interaction.

Everyday interactions can cause significant anxiety, self-consciousness and embarrassment because of a fear of being scrutinised or judged negatively by others. Social anxiety disorder can disrupt your life and affect your relationships, daily routines, work, school or other activities.

Typical social situations that can cause anxiety include:

→ Meeting new people.

→ Talking in meetings or in groups.

→ Starting conversations.

→ Talking to people in authority.

→ Being observed while working, eating or drinking (stare off mate!).

→ Going to school.

→ Shopping.

→ Being seen in public by neighbours or friends.

→ And my kryptonite, having to use public toilets.

I'm not claiming to be an academic or medical expert on the subject (I'm just an Autistic guy), but we can see how a lot of the traits of being Autistic are very similar to the traits of having social anxiety disorder, because autism is very much related to communication, social interaction, and all the many moments that go with communicating and interacting in a neurotypical world.

So if we already feel behind the eight ball in terms of neurotypical skills and abilities to thrive in a neurotypical world, then it's probably safe to say that entering the world without those skills, means soon enough we're likely to become weighed down with anxiety of one form or another.

At the core of that fear of social situations is usually embarrassment, but it runs deeper than that. There is also a strong sense of looking stupid, offending people, and the perceived judgement from saying the wrong thing or doing the wrong thing, regardless of the reality of those social situations. In other words, the threat posed by those social situations doesn't match *the fear* of the threat in those social situations.

Now this is where complications in forms of therapy may arise because a lot of the professional explanations and advice are created through the lens of neurotypical people experiencing social anxiety disorder. But as an Autistic person, this perceived threat that I could say the wrong thing at any moment is already my day-to-day life. I could actually argue that the threats are real because I'm an Autistic person trying to communicate in a neurotypical world with neurotypical people, so my chances of success are already slim at best. These situational threats are real; they are taken from experience and therefore in my opinion, are not out of proportion.

Now, I know that sounds a little over the top, but that's really what it is like in my experience. You fear going into those interactions because you anticipate you'll be scrutinised, judged, looked down on and somehow, you'll come out being embarrassed and looking bad. The level of discomfort is so high that you would do anything to avoid it. And therefore that anxiety can lead to avoidance; you'll do anything to avoid feeling that. You'll stay away from social interactions that disrupt your life and like a domino effect this avoidance will begin to affect so many areas of your life and the people in it.

> **Your anxiety can affect your family, your partner, your kids, your friends. It could affect your job or even your health. Your outside world becomes much smaller.**

An example from my life living with social anxiety disorder is something as simple as taking our weekly garbage bins to the curb. It's not that I don't like my neighbours or the people that live around me, that's just not true; they're all very nice and friendly. They say hello and wave and I awkwardly do something I can't explain in return. I'm pretty sure my Autistic brain is hardwired to only respond to neighbours in such a way that can only leave them with the impression that I am a troubled ex circus clown in rehab or a serial killer who exclusively preys on ants and small spiders.

But from my point of view, the idea that if I go outside to put the bins out or bring them in, and then another neighbour may also be outside and see me and want to talk to me, will cause me to decide to not go outside. Or I might check if the coast is clear first, to look around and check for "threats." It's not about them, it's about me. I'm not anxious about seeing *them*, I'm anxious about them seeing *me*, which poses the threat of interaction. It's a vicious cycle. One that I legitimately feel I can't do. I'll only go outside if I don't have to interact with anyone.

My Autistic son presents a similar dilemma for me to navigate. He is Autistic in his own unique way and frankly, is the opposite to me. He will walk up to anyone and just start talking to them. This is not good *Well, except for other ex-circus clowns from rehab, obviously.* for me. My goal is to avoid interactions at all cost, while his goal seems to be to meet and interact with every person he ever comes in contact with. If we're playing in the backyard and people walk by the front footpath, he could decide to just run up and start talking to them; that's the worst-case scenario for me.

My goal quickly becomes trying to get him into the house pronto. Or it might become "You're on your own, champ," and I'll retreat and get my wife to rescue the conversation because I don't want to be part of the interaction. I feel so anxious if I see that my son wants to go over and talk to people that I freak out and try to stop him which I know is not healthy.

I should not be stopping people in my life from talking to other people and that's not what I'm primarily trying to do. My aim is to prevent me from having to go and talk to them, smooth things over, or wrap up a conversation; I absolutely do not want to do any of those things. It's worrying enough that my son wants to interact with everyone, then I'm forced to interact with them, about their interaction with him, and honestly the word interaction has lost all meaning now. INTERACTION!

# GENERALISED ANXIETY DISORDER

The next form of anxiety to note, and another of my co-occurring conditions, is generalised anxiety disorder or GAD. GAD is a persistent and excessive worry about things. I call it the caveman anxiety because every moment of my life I feel like a caveman on constant lookout for predators. Thanks for nothing amygdala and get stuffed cortisol. People with GAD may anticipate disaster and find it difficult to control their worry.

Regardless of the situation, the worries generated are equally intense and persistent. People with GAD are overly concerned about basically everything. For me, I am continually in a really heightened state about everything in my life potentially going bad. I am in a constant state of fear and worry about work life, home life, and everything in between.

It's an exhausting, devastating form of anxiety to have because in essence, unlike social anxiety disorder where you can avoid the threat, with GAD you can't control your level of worrying about things that you can't avoid. So you can't control not worrying or worrying; you just worry. Like I said with the caveman analogy, you don't know if you're going to be attacked so you never let your guard down and relax.

The only problem is I'm not a caveman (at least not in the traditional *Homo sapiens* sense). I'm certainly not, as a rule, needing to protect myself or run away from attacks by wild animals (or other prehistoric creatures) but my brain still acts like I am. The amygdala is firing nonstop and on alert, which is just pumping my body with the stress hormone, cortisol. Great huh?

The best you can do is try to mitigate the impact of stressful situations with solutions, support and alternate versions of the scenario. For me, I try to go to the shops in the morning before the daily rush. I also avoid rush hour on the roads and try to stick to the same route for each destination. As an Autistic person with GAD, I can't help but imagine the worst-case scenario.

These thoughts just pop in there, like an equation. "This" could happen which could make "that" happen and on and on it goes. There's never really a break from it. And it's not like we get to the point of getting over the worry about a particular thing and move on to worry about something else after a while. We can worry about the same thing eternally. Being an Autistic person with GAD, I often find the sheer, constant and intense nature of this kind of worrying can really have a debilitating effect on my physical and mental health. This clearly interferes with not only my day-to-day life, but also my quality of life.

In order to help you understand the Autistic person in your life better, or the person in your life that may have this form of anxiety, ask yourself: *How would you feel mentally and physically if you thought something terrible was going to happen in every action or interaction of your day-to-day life?*

So more compassion and understanding is needed here peeps. Rather than rejecting our worries and fears outright, therefore devaluing our experience, view them from our point of view while offering a solution or support from your point of view.

# AGORAPHOBIA

The next form of anxiety that can be common in Autistic people is agoraphobia. Again, this can be a very similar experience to what Autistic people will feel from simply being Autistic. On a basic level, agoraphobia is where people are afraid to leave an environment that they consider to be safe.

Now, what rings true for Autistic people is knowing you have safe people and safe places every day, and they are core foundations for feeling good. When you head out into the world, you are going into areas you can't control, where you'll encounter sensory issues, interactions and neurotypical world challenges. A person with agoraphobia is unwilling to visit "unsafe" places because they're afraid that doing so will trigger anxiety or a panic attack.

> **In severe cases, someone with agoraphobia might consider their house to be the only safe place anywhere on the planet.**

As an Autistic person, I can absolutely relate to this. Shopping centres, big crowds at sporting halls, schools and busy streets aren't really a friendly stomping ground for an Autistic person or someone with agoraphobia. It's about the sensory input at these places; you are going to be physically, mentally, emotionally bombarded with stimuli and these sensations will be overwhelming. You could shut down, you could meltdown, or you could have a panic attack.

As an Autistic person, and also as a dad of an Autistic son, agoraphobia really resonates with me. It can be very hard to get our Autistic son to leave the house and go anywhere, even if we know he actually likes where he's going. This is a pretty common experience for many Autistic people.

# OBSESSIVE COMPULSIVE DISORDER

Another really common form of anxiety experienced by Autistic people is obsessive compulsive disorder, or OCD. The basic premise is along the lines of uncontrollable, repetitive, ritualistic behaviours that you feel compelled to perform to excess and they are time-consuming and distressing compulsions.

So a person with OCD may experience recurrent, persistent thoughts, images and impulses. Attached to this is the feeling that all these things are not wanted in our mind. They're intrusive. You don't wake up in the morning and say, "Hey, please fill my brain with actions that I'm compelled to perform on a repetitive basis!"

People with OCD are usually aware of the irrational and excessive nature of their obsessions and compulsions. However, they feel unable to control their obsessions or resist their compulsions. OCD causes the brain to get stuck on a particular thought or urge. For example, you may check the stove 20 times to make sure it's really turned off because you're terrified of burning down your house, or you may check the door is locked after you know you just locked it.

Or let's say I'm using the stovetop to cook dinner, right? I'm just using one burner, easy. But when I've finished and I turn that burner off, I'll turn every other burner off too. No, they weren't on, but I need to go along the whole panel of nobs and still do the motion of turning them off, even if I'm moving it to nothing, I'm just hitting resistance, I need to make sure that all the burners are off to satisfy the compulsion to know they are off.

I also have a pretty healthy obsession with symmetry, exactness, tidiness and orderliness. If you go to my space in the house you'll see it is not messy, not trashed, all things aligned, everything in its place. I can hear you saying, "But hang on Orion, how can that be? You have kids!"

And yes, there is no question that the most appropriate description of the majority of my house is chaotic. I would describe our playroom as a very colourful wasteland where toys and books go to die, and by die I mean a slow, torturous demise.

*Hey, how did you get into my book? Get out! It's for reading only. I write, you read. Got it?*

As an Autistic husband and father, I feel a strong pull towards tidying up after my family (I wrote family instead of kids just to annoy my wife. Sucked in Renee), yet I find myself becoming so overwhelmed by the constant family mess that I can struggle to know where to start. So, I tend to focus on my space to maintain straight lines and symmetry of objects and space, while doing the best I can with the rest of the wasteland/ house. Everything has its place in my space, and I know where everything is at all times. Someone entering my space, moving my things or worse still, taking my things without returning them to where they found them, will shake me to the core.

It's a really interesting notion that OCD is getting stuck on a particular thought or action and provides a behavioural pattern that has a soothing effect. For that moment, you are in control and I can really relate to that as an Autistic person. I use stimming as a way to regulate and soothe myself and in some ways OCD is another form of stimming for me. If there's a person in your life that has OCD—maybe they're Autistic with OCD—just understand that these impulses are beyond their control and this is where shaming and judging is unhelpful. Please just view it for what it is.

Anxiety is not a dirty word, and it's certainly something we as a community need to understand more about. The connection between autism and anxiety is apparent and understandable every way you look at it. The added presence of a diagnosed form of anxiety plays a really significant part in the day-to-day life of an Autistic person and their overall quality of life. Understanding the potential for this to occur and the added challenges it brings can help neurotypical people be more mindful and compassionate when the Autistic person in their life appears to be struggling. They might just need some extra help or support for whatever you or life might be asking of them.

I hope my own personal experiences have given you a little bit more of an insight into anxiety and its connection with autism. If they haven't I blame you, and you only.

## 📣 CLEANING FOR THE CLEANER

A family friend once complained to me that they had to spend so much time cleaning their house. "Who doesn't?" was my reaction. But then they said, "You don't understand, I was cleaning the house for the cleaner." This is not a joke, on the day their cleaner comes to clean their house, they must clean up parts of the house to ensure the house gets cleaned. The cleaner needs clean space to clean.

If you have to clean your house in order for the cleaner to clean your house you don't have a cleaner, you are the cleaner! In fact, you are your cleaner's cleaner. You're working for the cleaner whilst paying them money for them to be your boss.

You've already started cleaning, just finish it yourself and save some money.

# CHAPTER 7 | ANXIETY TRIGGERS

O ne of the reasons I'm so compelled to get this book into your hands is so you will take this knowledge into real life situations and relationships and be able to look at the moment in front of you with new eyes. You will have a whole new skillset to identify and support the Autistic person in your life (or yourself if you are Autistic) through moments that might test you or confuse you.

It's timely therefore to talk on a really practical level and point out some of the day-to-day triggers that can cause anxiety in an Autistic person. Keep in mind these things cause a *feeling* of anxiety; they do not cause a diagnosable form of anxiety, which requires an assessment by a healthcare practitioner.

You might not have realised it, but these common situations and/or the ensuing emotions can cause anxiety for an Autistic person…

- Phone calls – making, receiving, talking, expecting.

- New places and new people.

- Change in routine or unexpected change of plans.

- Not enough time to spend on your special interest.

- Interruptions, personal demands, and outside forces getting in the way of completing a task.

- Challenges with executive function getting in the way of completing tasks.

- Feeling unprepared or unable to complete a task.

- Not enough alone time.

- Ambiguous or unclear directions, instructions or questions.

- Too many directions, instructions or questions at once.

- Too many stressors or demands.

- Neurotypical expectations or non-specific expectations.

- Being misunderstood or misrepresented.

- Being patronised or talked down to.

- Strong reactions from people, or strong personalities.

- Strong emotions of others.

- Being a part of or near confrontation or arguments.

- Having mistakes pointed out or being ridiculed.

- Using public transport or travelling in general.

If you're Autistic and feel anxious a lot, do you have anxiety or is it just because you're Autistic in the way you perceive and view the world? It's a complicated conversation. Let's break down the "what" and the "why" of common anxiety triggers.

## PHONE CALLS

The first anxiety trigger out there that can potentially rear its head at any moment of the day is phone calls. This includes making phone calls, receiving phone calls, talking on the phone in general, and especially being thrust into them suddenly.

If you asked me to call a guy today from some particular company to find out when something would be delivered, the chances of that happening are astronomically low. It's not because I don't want to do something for you; I'd love to. But the sheer anxiety built up over making that phone call can be debilitating. The endless round of questions begin in my head.

These thoughts create confusion, pressure and anxiety that can have a physical effect. So it's more than likely that the phone call will not be made.

Similarly, when people call me, even if I recognise the number, I don't want to talk. It's not that I don't want to talk to them; I don't want to answer that phone call for so many reasons. The anxiety of wondering: *Why are they calling me? Do they need something from me that is going to cause even more anxiety? Are they calling because they want to come into my space today, right now, when I'm doing something important to me? Are they calling because they want to talk to me about something I don't want to talk about? What will change after this phone call? Why are they calling?!* There are so many things that go through my mind just around phone calls. They trigger so much anxiety.

Here's a tip for Autistic people reading—you should change your voicemail greeting on your phone to something like this:

"Hi, thanks for calling. My preferred method of communication is through text or email. So if it's possible that you don't need to leave a voice message or talk to me on the phone, could you please continue this conversation on email or by texting me? Thank you so much for your understanding. Beep."

Actually, if you say beep there will be two beeps, your beep followed by the phone beep, so maybe ditch the beep. Yours, not the phone's... wait, is that even possible?

One advantage to the modern digital age is that there are so many communication options out there that can actually help Autistic people to communicate in a medium they find comfortable, and can allow them to forge relationships in many different ways without the anxiety. The idea that you must have voice conversations (let alone face-to-face conversations in person) is often unnecessary. Yes, it helps to learn the skills to do this when required, but it's not the only option.

There are ways around the unhelpful phone call, so let's use them! Better still, ban the phone call! Most people only call because they're too lazy to type anyway.

# UNFAMILIAR ENVIRONMENTS AND PEOPLE

I know I've talked about this a lot—the challenge of new places and new people. It's similar to phone calls, in that it raises too many unknown variables in what it's going to be like, what's going to happen and what's going to be expected of me.

One of the clear diagnostic criteria for being diagnosed Autistic comes down to different evaluations around social interaction and social communication; the types of moments neurotypical people don't even think about. Firstly, going somewhere new means you're leaving your safe place. Even if it's just around the corner, you are still far from your safe place.

Let's imagine a totally fictional new place that I've never been to before. I will quickly feel anxiety about not knowing how long it will take to get there. *How long will it take to get back? Who will be there? Where are the nearest public toilets? Will they be open? Will they be clean, safe, usable? What will I do if I have to go to the toilet? Where will I eat? What will they serve? Will I have to talk to people?*

Argh, new people! Yes, there'll be new people there. So, you want me to go to a new place I've never been to before, I'm not even sure about the toilet situation and there's going to be new people and I'm supposed to just interact with them? Do you see how the situation is spiralling further away from our safe place?

An important tip for parents and carers of Autistic kids if you are going to take your Autistic kid to a new place: number one, remember the idea in itself is going to cause massive anxiety.

> **Don't place expectations on them to interact with new people.**

Remember, that can be a challenge for them with people they know and love, let alone new people. Let them take things at a pace they feel comfortable with. If they hear people talking about something that interests them, this might be a natural way for them to be drawn in to offer something to the conversation. Don't start with, "Come and say hello to this person immediately!"

The same goes for partners of Autistic people. If your partner is Autistic and you say, "Hey, let's go to this party," and you try to acknowledge that it's a new place with new people by adding in, "You'll be okay, I'll be right there." But just getting themselves to walk through the door is a massive goal for your partner and this leaves them heaving with anxiety.

Then you get angry because they're being quiet or standoffish or stuck in a corner or treating people a little coldly (in your mind) or replying in monosyllables at people's attempts to engage with them. This is all because they're pumping with anxiety.

It's your call. You can keep forcing this kind of stuff upon your kids or your partner, but don't get angry when it results in anxiety and they act accordingly.

# CHANGE IN PLANS

This trigger covers countless situations really. Change of plans, change of routine, unexpected changes, basically life just doing its thing and throwing curve balls. Take, for example, my Autistic son. For a neurotypical child (and maybe you have similar memories), everyday changes or things occurring that you didn't expect barely register on their reaction scale, let alone create anxiety.

However, for my Autistic son, panic and anxiety can be triggered by a change in school bus driver, not being able to sit in the same seat on the bus (he refers to it as "his seat"), substitute teachers, losing the safety of his best friend or teacher for a new teacher each year, or simply hearing the school bell while still in the toilet. And don't get me started on the anxiety triggered by the school sporting carnival and social events like fancy dress and dances. In fact, our son was anxious about grade 3 school camp from the moment he found out about it in grade 1.

It doesn't even need to be wholly unexpected either. Let's say every Monday, I have the house to myself to record a video. However, on Sunday one of my kids gets sick. Now, I know that tomorrow (Monday) I am going to be home with our sick child and I won't be able to work on my videos. You might think that's a somewhat "expected" change of plans. I knew on the

Sunday what was going to happen on the Monday, however it's still going to fill me with anxiety because I'll start to think:

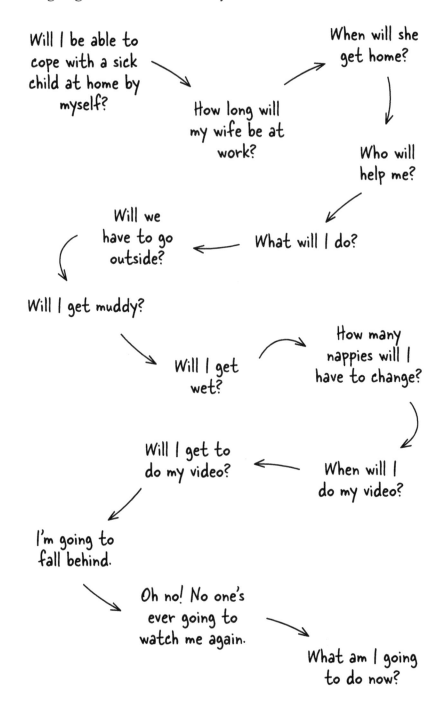

These thoughts just snowball. Regardless of knowing ahead of time or not knowing, it's still an immense trigger that compounds but at a much more successful rate than a term deposit.

I totally get that life changes suddenly; that's life. It has to happen and as an Autistic dad, you have to roll with the punches. (Which for me means despite Rocky Balboa-level training, I fail to block a single punch and am knocked out in the first round.) But it's important to understand that in rolling with those punches, while it (hopefully) helps the family, which is the goal and that's great, it is also going to cause different levels of anxiety depending on the person.

Like a domino effect, that anxiety is going to cause different levels of potentially negative responses or feelings or behaviours that other people might not feel comfortable with. But hey, what do you want? You can't have it both ways. I can roll with the punches at a cost. So you can take it to the bank, life will throw curve balls and I'll stagger through them any way I can, but there will be a fallout.

## 📢 TAKE THAT TO THE BANK...

I've had people say to me, "You can take that to the bank." Take what to the bank? I just gave you words. Where's the Bank of Words? I'd like to withdraw one hundred thousand words please. SECURITY! Let's say I invite a friend of mine over for a BBQ on the weekend. And they accept and follow up said acceptance with, "You can take that to the bank." Are you suggesting your promise to come over is bankable? So, let's say I go to the bank, explain that my friend said that they are coming over to my place on the weekend and I'd like to deposit that promise into my account. Forget security, they're calling a SWAT team after that. You can't deposit words at the bank, and you can take that to the bank.

If something unexpected happens, it's a trigger, so just take what you know now about anxiety, and tread carefully. By the way, I am unsure if anyone in the history of baseball has indeed staggered through a curve ball, given they're holding a bat and attempting to hit a ball coming at them at speed in a curve–like fashion... nah... forget it.

# NOT HAVING ENOUGH TIME FOR YOUR SPECIAL INTEREST

Following closely behind the "unexpected" trigger is not having enough time to spend on your special interest, your passion. So, if my child's sick, I won't be able to spend much or any time working on my special interests, my passion, which is creating content, which also happens to be my bread and butter and my contribution to my household. That's clearly going to raise my levels of anxiety.

But even if we take away the career and income side of things, say if your partner doesn't have a special interest that's related to work or generates an income, it doesn't matter. They are passionate about doing certain things, whether that time is productive in your eyes or not. It's their particular passion, it's their special interest and they are going to need genuine and ample time on a daily basis to spend on that particular interest.

And the same goes for parents and carers of Autistic kids—they need more time than you probably imagine to "work" on their interests. A whole lifetime of ideas goes on in their head thinking about their special interest, where they are up to with it, what else they need to find out about it; they are just waiting for the next time they can dive into it again. Life (and often school) are just basically getting in the way of them doing it!

So, if there is a change in plans or routines, or an interruption that means there is less time to spend on their passion because there are other things keeping them busy, that's going to cause anxiety. For me it can also cause anger and resentment. Personally, working on special interests or passions is oxygen for an Autistic person. It's our lifeblood. It literally feels like the reason we were born.

Here's a curly one for you from my Autistic brain. Are we good at the things that just happen to be our passions, or are they our passions because we are good at them?

So not enough time can come across to us like a life-or-death situation. I know it isn't (well, I've come to know it isn't, I guess), but something inside us tells us there's nothing

*I can wait; email me via my website when you're done.*

more important, and nothing that makes us feel so good, so comfortable and more natural than focusing our energy on a special interest; anything else has the potential to trigger anxiety.

## INTERRUPTIONS AND DEMANDS

All right, so the next anxiety triggers I want to talk about that can really test children and adults are interruptions or demands placed upon an Autistic person. Demands and stressors piling up one after the other is another unavoidable part of life.

If you have an Autistic person in your life and they are trying to complete a task, it doesn't even have to be special interests, it could be work, homework or any kind of household task. Whatever the task they are concentrating on to complete, do not interrupt them. Do not place other demands on them. Do not allow other outside forces to block them or stop them from completing that task.

The only thing important to me is completing this task. Now that might seem completely inappropriate and possibly an overreaction in your eyes. However, it's the way my brain works and all I'm trying to do is just get these tasks ticked off. I don't feel I have the ability to start a task and come back to complete it later.

There are exceptions to what I'm talking about. I'm not going to write a university thesis in one sitting. Obviously not… again. But if I say, today my task is to do x amount and then something else comes up, that's going to cause anxiety for me. So, pushing back and insisting I stop before I have finished the task at hand is not going to help you, and it will very likely trigger anxiety in an Autistic person.

# CHALLENGES WITH EXECUTIVE FUNCTION

Another anxiety trigger in Autistic people relates to challenges around executive function and completing tasks. While we just spoke of interruptions and personal demands which people control, this relates to our own executive functioning being put under pressure by those changes. In general, executive functioning relates to one's mental ability to plan, focus attention, process, remember and juggle multiple tasks.

This is something that you might take for granted, but an Autistic person can really struggle with executive function. When you ask me a question, I need time to process your question, and also to process my answer because remember, when I respond naturally as my Autistic self, it might not go down well with you or with the neurotypical world. This is a lesson Autistic people learn the hard way as they grow from being an Autistic child to an Autistic adult in a neurotypical world.

So, our executive functioning can falter or fail when put under the stress of change. This stress can appear when juggling too many tasks or from increased changes like school holidays or winter illnesses, as an example. Therefore, along with knowing we have to try and deal with the anxiety of the change itself, we are anxious about the consequences on our executive functioning that we were relying on to get tasks done!

A simple example might be around a time management issue. You might say to me, "I'm sorry buddy, it's dinner time now. You're going to have to complete the rest of that after dinner." Immediately my brain thinks:

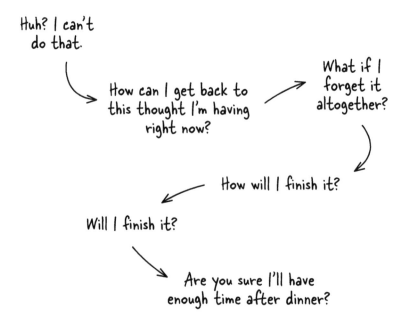

Having to replan the whole task becomes overwhelming. Executive functioning is challenging even when everything is in alignment, so changes add pressure and heightens our anxiety further.

# FEELING UNABLE TO COMPLETE TASKS

On a bigger scale, another anxiety trigger I've found as an Autistic person is thinking about completing tasks that may involve a lot of steps or processes. Immediately I have this really strong sense of being unprepared, inept, totally incapable of actually completing said task which triggers anxiety straight away. In a way, this trigger can be helped by support.

For example, when I was at university studying law, my wife was incredibly important in supporting me in this experience. Law school assignments as a rule are pretty intense. Okay, primary school assignments were pretty intense for me due to my own inappropriately high standards and expectations.

What's interesting is that even though I studied law at university, I still don't think I'm intelligent. But overall, as an adult student I felt confident at the thought of assignments and that I should do well and get good marks. Despite this, when we would be given an assignment and I initially read the instructions and the structure I had to follow, I was instantly consumed with the strongest feeling that there was no way I could do this! Absolutely no way. I wasn't smart enough or good enough. I just didn't know this stuff enough to even attempt it.

There was no way I was prepared to do it. I couldn't. Not going to happen. It's too much!

Enter a wonderful wife/parent/carer who can help you by saying, "Hang on, it's actually no different to all the other assignments you've completed. Sure, the topic's different but it's the same principle. You just do your research, step by step. Do one thing at a time and work from there."

> **Telling an Autistic person to try being more "Zen"**
> **is like telling a lion to try being more kangaroo.**

One analogy that did work for me was thinking about an astronaut on a spacewalk. When an astronaut has to carry out running repairs and maintenance on infrastructure in the vastness of space, they must wear oven mitts for gloves while handling very small tools and implements that if dropped could rip their suit and... well they're in space. There is only one way to do things; one step at a time. A spacewalk may take 12 hours just to remove a few screws, replace a component and put the screws back in place. But you wouldn't know because all they focus on is one tiny task at a time: one bolt at a time.

The good news for us is we don't have to do our task in space wearing oven mitts! As an Autistic person, when I am given a seemingly enormous task, I am blind at first to the stepping-stones within the task. If not for the support of others, I would be forever stranded on Mount Trigger where the only thing you can catch is anxiety and the ability to be overwhelmed and catastrophise everything.

# NOT ENOUGH ALONE TIME

Another really important anxiety trigger, at least for me as an Autistic person, is not enough alone time. Now I know this may sound impractical for many reasons to neurotypical people. You might be tempted to remind me, "You're a husband and a father, what do you mean you need more alone time? What did you think was going to happen? You're not single. You're part of the family."

It's impractical and I get it. What I'm saying is while I acknowledge that responsibility, I can't pretend I'm not Autistic. I have a different brain. I can't be neurotypical.

> My only way of keeping myself on track, regulated and a good dad and husband, is to maintain regular alone time. It doesn't have to be for long.

For me, as an adult I might just need five minutes in a room by myself to bring myself back. And then I'm ready to go and play the same repetitive game with the kids downstairs. But either way, whether it's a child or an adult, not enough alone time or withholding alone time from an Autistic person in your life is going to trigger anxiety any day of the week. And once again, this is not a win-win for anyone.

# AMBIGUOUS COMMUNICATION

An important anxiety trigger in general, right across the Autistic population, is being communicated to in ambiguous terms, unclear language, unclear directions, ambiguous questions, open-ended questions, or hypothetical questions. This type of language is extremely triggering for Autistic people.

If you're feeling frustrated with the Autistic person in your life, really ask yourself, *How clearly did I phrase that sentence or question to them? Did I give them all the details they need to understand the wider context of why I'm saying or asking something, and what it means for them in the next minute, hour, or day?*

> **Reframing common expressions and passive messages into clear language can make a huge difference in positive, successful communication and more time for enjoyment, not misunderstandings.**

So, my number one advice is to be clear. Make sure that your questions, your directions and your language are unambiguous. Make sure it is precise, explicit, black-and-white, 100% understood. My wife will sometimes make observations, and unbeknownst to me, those observations are actually directions or instructions.

If she says, "Wow, the toy room is absolutely trashed," before she leaves for work, this is actually secret code for, *Can you tidy this room up today please?* Unambiguous language could avoid the riveting drama when she gets home. Observe.

Wife: "Why are the toys still over the toy room? You can't see the floor, what happened Orion?"

Orion looking perplexed: "What do you mean what happened? I agreed with you. There are toys everywhere. What did I miss?"

Wife rolls eyes to the ceiling: "Well, this morning I said what's with the toy room and I can't believe how messy it is and I thought that meant you would pick it up. I was saying 'pick it up'."

Orion rolls eyes to the ceiling: "But you didn't say 'pick up the toys'. You just made an observation, 'Oh look, the toy room is trashed' and I agree, it is."

You see the fun we have? Granted my wife has a different word for that but you probably don't need to be exposed to such words. Yep, my wife has quite the potty mouth.

## TOO MANY INSTRUCTIONS AT ONCE

Too many instructions or directions at once is another anxiety trigger. I still often wonder why it is that neurotypical people think we can be asked or instructed to do multiple things and somehow all that information will be processed.

Let's be practical and acknowledge there's absolutely nothing wrong with making a list; it's actually really helpful. If you write a list of the top three things that could be achieved by the Autistic person in your life today, it's more likely to be achieved than verbally yelling it over your shoulder as you walk out the door.

Writing it down leaves less room for error, so you could write:

*Orion, please wash the coloured load of clothing today.*

Write "the coloured load," not just "do the washing"—the more detail, the better the outcome.

*Please wash the coloured load of dirty clothing, tidy the toy room and wash the dirty dishes. Have a great day Orion!*

Writing it well beforehand like this helps us adjust to the day ahead. It means we won't be so overwhelmed with anxiety at the thought of doing those things, so that when we have (hopefully) finished them, we still have some energy, drive or motivation leftover to actually still do something we wanted to do that day.

As a parent or carer of an Autistic child you may (without realising it) be placing neurotypical expectations on your child. Now I know the first thing that most people will say back to me is, "That's rubbish!" But I still bet you do it sometimes. I know my wife and I probably do it too. We know our child is Autistic, but it doesn't mean sometimes subconsciously we still don't have neurotypical expectations. Sometimes it might slip out.

You might say, "Why can't you just sit down like a normal person?" This is an example of a subconscious expectation.

Now we know they can't sit down in a conventional fashion because they're not neurotypical, they're Autistic. Looking for alternatives is the best solution; perhaps you could find them a wobble chair or cushion, find them something else to sit or stand on, or encourage them to redirect their interest onto a different task or activity entirely.

Placing unrealistic expectations or neurotypical expectations on an Autistic child or adult will always trigger levels of anxiety.

## BEING MISUNDERSTOOD

I can absolutely relate to the anxiety trigger of being misunderstood or misrepresented. I won't make assumptions about every Autistic person, but in my experience as an Autistic person I find that in almost every conversation (and this includes with my family), I'm almost always misunderstood, be that my words, tone of voice, or body language.

I don't think I've ever had a conversation or said something that was taken the way I intended it. There are many issues here, such as my tone as we explored briefly earlier. My tone can come across to some people as over the top or aggressive or heard as sounding negative.

This is something that most Autistic people will learn to understand very quickly; when communicating with others, it seems like there's something missing. I wasn't trying to offend you. What I was trying to say was a good thing, it was positive. But I apologise. All I'm doing is apologising. I don't even know what I'm apologising for.

# STRONG REACTIONS AND PERSONALITIES

As an Autistic person, a known anxiety trigger for me is being near a strong reaction from someone or being near people with strong personalities. This is an interesting scenario because I am perceptive to an undercurrent here that normally I wouldn't be.

What I mean is, if there is someone who is a little like me in their character (although not Autistic), someone who is a bit louder than the usual, a bit more vocal, a bigger personality who really wants me to hear and agree with them and who unconsciously is invading my physical and mental space, I instinctively push away from them. I am almost repelled by a magnetic force that we don't match. They rub me the wrong way. I feel much more at ease and comfortable with people who make me feel at ease and comfortable.

With people with strong personalities or who are more of an in-your-face person, it doesn't mean they shouldn't be like that, it's just that personally I am filled with anxiety and discomfort around them. I am on alert, unsure what they will do or say next or when their spotlight will suddenly turn to me with expectations. I don't mind the spotlight occasionally but it must be my own choosing. So I find this loud, confronting energy exhausting to be around.

Similarly with strong reactions; they cause anxiety because hypersensitivity in Autistic people can manifest in feeling the emotions of others more deeply and stronger than potentially neurotypical people would. Not so much the person feeling it but feeling other people's reactions around them. We might come across like we're feeling nothing, but again, the truth is a whole different thing.

So, these strong emotions, these strong reactions, these strong personalities can really heighten anxiety in some Autistic people.

## CONFRONTATION

Further to this (and it's a bit like the paradox of strong personalities repelling), confrontation is another anxiety trigger. Confrontations, confrontational situations or being in or around arguments are hell on the nervous system and we can get fidgety as soon as we sense them coming.

I know it's strange because some Autistic people, like me for example, can come across as always argumentative. People often say, "Why are you arguing with me?" But I'm not arguing. In my mind we're just having a conversation. With every neurotypical person that I have a conversation with where I'm thinking we're having a really great, in-depth inquisitive conversation, they are thinking that it's a full-on argument!

What is it with neurotypical people? We can only talk if it's friendly and lightweight? That's not talking honestly; always staying in the friendly and comfortable zone would involve lying and deception for an Autistic person, and not saying what we think at all times is virtually impossible.

The confrontational situations that can trigger anxiety are meeting with people you find you clash with, some phone calls, having to return an item at the store you bought it from, or being confrontational around Autistic people.

Being around or in arguments can absolutely heighten our levels of anxiety.

## HAVING MISTAKES POINTED OUT TO YOU

From one contradiction to another, this is a classic one. As an Autistic person, I tend to be a real stickler. I'm compelled to point out things that are wrong. I have a strong sense of right and wrong, moral justice, all that type of stuff. But in addition to that, I just have a strong sense of right or wrong in petty, picky things. So, if there's anyone on the planet who is going to point out mistakes or things that are wrong, it's potentially Autistic people.

But guess what? A known anxiety trigger, certainly for me, is having our mistakes pointed out. And it goes without saying, being ridiculed, patronised or talked down to for mistakes or errors clearly heightens anxiety in Autistic people. I'm sure it probably triggers neurotypical people as well. And fair enough.

For some reason though, it seems to really trigger a heightened sense of anxiety in Autistic people. It might be related to the strong sense of right and wrong we feel.

> **When we point out mistakes it's because our brain sees errors and mistakes like flashing red lights. It's not personal; we are being helpful in our eyes.**

We see them clearly and I should point out, we see the solutions too—what should happen or needs to happen to fix it. That's all part of an Autistic brain, we know the rules (well… we're familiar with some) and we can clearly see when they aren't working or something isn't right when we look at the situation in front of us.

So, it's understandable that we don't want to be that person who has erred, right? We don't want to be the person who's created something that is wrong or made an error or a mistake because we don't like that. Our brain looks for those to fix them.

We can think to ourselves, *I hope this isn't a mistake. I hope this isn't wrong.* And often that's why I'll go through things multiple times. I will read an email three times before sending it and then once it's sent, I'll reread it as if I were the person receiving the email. Which is weird because it's already sent. But when something amiss is pointed out to me, it validates the idea that I have made a mistake, I am wrong, I've created an error, and I should have seen that. That then heightens criticism of ourselves and our anxiety further.

# TRAVELLING AND PUBLIC TRANSPORT

Technically this could come under unfamiliar environments, which we covered earlier, yet it really deserves some space dedicated to the challenges of travelling. For parents and carers of Autistic kids, I know you already know what travelling and public transport can mean for Autistic people and the people around them.

My wife and I have been on holidays with our Autistic son and our younger son. Six hours into the first day we were already saying to each other, "Is it time to go home yet? Let's wrap this up my friend. Let's just book a flight and go home. This is not working."

We somehow pushed through and by the next day or perhaps the day after that, we've learnt a lot about the unpredictable and tiring nature of travelling, yet we found a rhythm, and started to notice the adventure we were having. By the time we got home, although it was never easy or relaxing or enjoyable, somehow it became the best thing that's ever happened to the kids.

Not that it's a high benchmark though. My son sustained a deep facial laceration, which required an ambulance ride to the hospital and multiple stitches, yet he still talks about how good the holiday was. Obviously, the challenges of travelling clearly come down to sensory, Hypersensitivity and social communication challenges, including all the different sensory inputs of transport and travelling and the possible delays and interruptions.

And airports! Oh my goodness, don't get me started. It's a clear anxiety trigger, but preparing and having "what if" conversations beforehand can potentially help you to be a little bit more proactive, protective, caring and understanding around not only yourself and your family, but the Autistic people in your life.

There have also been some exciting developments such as the Hidden Disabilities Sunflower Lanyard Scheme that runs in some airports overseas and is starting to spread throughout Australia. In essence, there are sunflower wristbands or lanyards you wear around your neck with an ID card, which indicates in a really subtle way to the airport staff and services that you are perhaps Autistic or have a hidden disability and may benefit from certain supports from staff to help you move through the airport environment. This is by no means a perfect system, but it's a start. In the end it all comes down to people, not programs.

By simply understanding some of the more specific anxiety triggers for Autistic people, not only will it help the Autistic person in your life but really, it helps your quality of life as well because everyone feels a little bit calmer and that's a win-win for everyone.

## 📢 MUTUAL AGREEMENT

The phrase "mutual agreement" is kind of redundant. An agreement is an agreement between two or more parties, which presumably is mutual or it wouldn't be an agreement. It would be a disagreement.

# CHAPTER 8 | AUTISTIC MASKING

My friend, we have arrived at a significant turning point in our journey. There is a major aspect that we are yet to examine closely in the daily life of an Autistic person: Autistic masking.

Once my mission is complete, and people in all areas of society and walks of life can spot the evidence of it, you may never look at an Autistic person the same way again. Building up your understanding and appreciation of Autistic people is what I'm all about. Well, that and coffee: I am all about coffee. Quick clarification, I'm all about good coffee. Anyway, back to masking.

I'm super excited about getting to this point because while Autistic masking is something that all Autistic people know intimately, I'm convinced the non-Autistic community can't get their head around the level of stress, pressure, and the energy we expel on a daily basis to fit in. Even if you say, "Wait a sec, everyone feels that pressure to fit in," I would agree that most people on the planet are drawn to the herd. We instinctively seek the safety and comfort of others to protect us from the prehistoric dangers our brains still fear.

But what if you were born unable to be accepted into the herd? What if your best self was an outcast, let alone your true self? Autistic people have come to realise that the only realistic and sometimes effective way to receive the approval and acceptance of others is to suppress our true Autistic selves—to hide any manifestation of our Autistic brain, to mask any sign of our differences.

> **In essence, masking is the act of camouflaging the difference between what is happening to an Autistic person on the inside and how they look or seem on the outside.**

Masking is any effort to suppress an Autistic feature, trait or difference from being expressed and seen. This could mean suppressing repetitive behaviours, noises, stimming or special interests, or pretending to follow a conversation without showing the stress, confusion and panic going on in our minds. Masking is a choice, but only because the neurotypical world seemingly rejects our differences. At its core masking is a compulsion to try and imitate neurotypical behaviour to avoid unwanted attention or engagement, rejection and judgement (and so avoid the heightened feelings that go along with all of that).

It is human instinct to try and fit in, which for an Autistic person generally means trying to come across "normal" in a neurotypical sense. For me, this means I often force myself to make eye contact with the person I'm talking to. It means suppressing my desire (or need) to talk about my special interest. It means talking to a stranger even though I don't want to, or talking to a person who knows someone close to me and displays a familiarity I do not feel, and I respond in a forced way that does not follow my natural instincts.

**Masking is a lifetime of hiding our authentic Autistic selves from the world.**

Masking is a lifetime of living a lie for the comfort of others, while our true selves rot away in eternal exile. I only mask because I have to. I don't choose to mask as my preferred way of living day-to-day. My preference is for the world to accept me for me and allow me to be my Autistic self with my many differences. But I know the fallout/consequences when I do that. In case you don't, they're not good. Not good for anyone. And the mental, physical and emotional toll of masking can be profound for Autistic people.

**Q:** Why do Autistic people mask? What's the point? Why bother? Why spend our entire lives acting like someone we're not?

**A:** To fit into a neurotypical world, so we feel accepted, wanted and appreciated.

This isn't rocket science; we're suppressing our true selves because the majority of people on the planet, which can include family and friends, don't accept us for our true selves. They're only prepared to deal with the cookie cutter, sugar-coated, neurotypical version of ourselves. They don't want the real stuff.

I'm unable to be myself. If you need reminding, being my true Autistic self means I will inadvertently "do" things to people without having any intention to. You know what I mean. I may anger, offend, upset, put out or put people off; I never seem to say or do the right things, which becomes a conundrum.

An Autistic person is caught in the limbo of being yourself and never fitting in or trying to mask your true self to fit in, to be accepted. Forcing myself to make eye contact when you are talking to me is masking. I don't like eye contact. But I do it so that you don't think I'm not listening, not interested, don't care about the conversation, or trying to be rude. What's most surprising for some people to hear is that I often need to look away during a conversation to process what I'm hearing and to properly engage and respond. You can have your precious eye contact; you just won't get me actually engaged in the conversation.

I know most people don't care about the special interests of Autistic people, so we suppress talking about it. But when I can unmask in my videos and podcasts, I can express the things that I want to talk about and my opinions and interests in any way my brain naturally takes the discussion. But if I were to talk like that to your face, giving my side of the conversation free rein which may mean me talking happily until I'm blue in the face, and my opinion may make you happy or angry but either way, I'm not thinking about the consequences. I'm not masking.

When I see someone in public who I don't really know well, let's say a partner or a relative of someone close to me, I force myself to engage because they usually make contact very quickly with little hesitation; there's a wave, a smile, a change of direction as they veer over to say hello. I force myself to try and do the small talk with them even though I fail miserably.

Why is this so hard for me? Because I am Autistic. I feel uncomfortable talking around people, or talking to people who I don't really know, or who I'm not comfortable with, or who I believe won't accept me. Yet I will force myself to do this to make them feel better, to make them feel more comfortable, to make them not think, *What is wrong with this guy? He just completely blew me off!*

But, you know what? I didn't, I'm Autistic. I'm masking my true self. My thought process is closer to, *Oh my goodness, I think I know that person, but I don't know what they're going to say to me. Hide behind this aisle Orion!* Then they'll walk closer so I quickly move behind the next aisle and the next, and it becomes so nerve wracking that I'll just drop my groceries and get out.

I know neurotypical people generally understand and follow conversational and behavioural conventions, which means they don't always say or do exactly what they think or want to do, but these conventions are things they can learn to adapt to over time. Most neurotypical adults can learn to know and accept what they should and shouldn't say and do in most situations and it's not something they give much thought to as they get older.

However, as an Autistic person, we can struggle to decipher these unwritten social rules. Aside from figuring out what they mean, we must forever suppress what we want to say, suppress our natural instincts and desires, by constantly masking.

> **Constantly masking. Always. Forever.**
> **I'm exhausted just thinking about it.**

## DETRIMENTAL EFFECTS OF MASKING

Masking is physically, emotionally, and mentally exhausting. It can lead to meltdowns, shutdowns, burnout, anxiety, and depression to name just a few. All to fit in with the neurotypical world, and even after all that effort is expelled to mask our true Autistic selves, inevitably we still fail. We lose friends. We lose relationships. We lose jobs. The cost is never-ending and sometimes profound.

As an Autistic person, I've been wearing a mask to protect myself for as long as I can remember. The longer-term damage caused by hiding or camouflaging our true selves can be devastating. You forget who your true self is.

**Identity crisis: Who is the real you?**

I get it, everyone can relate to the quest behind discovering, "Who am I?" But for Autistic people it's not a choice, or a "learning" experience to "discover" ourselves.

For me, as an Autistic person diagnosed later in life, I was forced to confront the reality that I had been living under a mask my whole life. This raised the question: if I'd been masking for a lifetime to fit in because I thought I was a bad person who didn't deserve what others had, **who was under the mask?** And was I even capable of taking it off?

So, the result is worse than if you could just be yourself from the start. Masking takes effort and energy and that drains you over a long period of time. Nowadays for me, after a while I don't mask as much with friends as I assume they accept me for me. But that is an exception; I've lost many "friends" in the past from being myself.

If the world just understood me better, and accepted me as an Autistic person, maybe I'd be able to be myself. People would say, "No, no, don't be offended by Orion, he's Autistic. He's very upfront. He's very honest. His words sound really frank and honest, maybe a bit harsh, but he does it for the right reasons. His brain thinks in open and direct ways of communicating."

Now I'm talking about myself in the third person, and it's kind of creepy, but you get my point, right? Clearly, my preference, as it is for every Autistic person, is for the world to accept us, and understand and embrace our true Autistic selves, and allow us to be ourselves with our many differences.

> How would you feel if you had to spend your
> entire life being someone you are not in order
> to be accepted and to fit in... yet knowing you
> will never fit in?

# MASKING AND EARLY INTERVENTION THERAPIES

I have my own personal beliefs and theories about the connection between masking and early intervention therapies. It's a tough subject to tackle because intervention therapies give many parents a sense of relief and support that they are doing all they can to help their Autistic child get the best start they can. Unfortunately it's not that simple.

For Autistic adults, intervention therapies and support services are nowhere near as common as what is potentially available for kids following a diagnosis (there still isn't enough support for them either but one argument at a time!).

If you have a child that receives a diagnosis, as my wife and I did when our first-born son was five years old, soon after the diagnosis the child receives referrals to therapies such as occupational health therapy, speech therapy, psychology, and physiotherapy, commonly referred to as early intervention therapies. Now for an adult, when you get a diagnosis like I did as an alleged grown man, I was given a diagnosis on a piece of paper—but that was it.

I can go on forever about the lack of adult support but for now, my point is that I lived these experiences through my son who did receive various therapies. And my overwhelming impression was the core of his intervention therapies were people trying to teach my Autistic son how *not* to act or look Autistic.

When he is Autistic in an outward, noticeable way, in a way that people think, *Oh he's not normal*, intervention therapies try to teach him to cut that Autistic stuff off as it starts occurring, and come across normal, to not act Autistic. Therefore to me, the connection between early intervention and masking is one and the same. In my opinion, some early intervention therapies are pure acting classes teaching Autistic kids how to play the role of a neurotypical person. To assimilate. To fit in.

But the situation becomes more complicated for Autistic kids when they soon learn that failure to mask can cause them to lose friends. Autistic kids are growing up in this world learning that for them, masking equals friends, NOT masking equals losing friends.

> Look behind you.

So while I can sit here and say my son needs the entire community to develop a broader understanding of people with differences, rather than getting people with differences to be taught how to act "normal," I also know that it won't happen overnight. But it will happen.

Trying to "normalise" is quite entrenched behaviour with most likely good intentions. Take an Australian-produced worldwide television show for example, which explores the romantic lives of Autistic people and other neurodivergent people as they prepare to go on a date with someone. The show brought in an "expert," a counsellor who was effectively teaching the Autistic person how to act on a date: "Here's how you must act on a date, for your date to go well." Not the common-sense advice, "Just be yourself. If they don't like you for you, they're not the right person. Just be you, and they'll love you, mate."

I wholly disagree with the premise that you would need to coach Autistic people how to not be Autistic in order to improve the chances that a date will go well. Even more perplexing was for the Autistic people who went on these television dates with other Autistic people, they were also instructed how to act on a date with another Autistic person!

We're teaching Autistic people how to not be Autistic, in order to date Autistic people, and that's a show? My wife is not Autistic; she's neurotypical. I just found her, she found me, and we fit. So as an Autistic person, you may find another Autistic person and you'll fit, or you may well find someone completely different to you, and you'll fit. Either way, if they don't like you for you, it's not going to work.

Here's a test for you: imagine if this whole scenario of being compelled to act differently was on the other foot.

Starting tomorrow, all parents of neurotypical or non-Autistic kids will need to enrol their child into regular early interventional therapies, so they can be taught how to act around Autistic kids, because they're just not behaving in the way that makes Autistic kids comfortable. They don't understand how Autistic kids want them to act. They're just not very good at reading Autistic kids. They're just not very good at talking to Autistic kids. They're not very good around Autistic kids. This therapy will teach them how to act Autistic.

How about it? How would that sit with you? I know it's a long road but we have to start somewhere. Let's start by recognising the very act of masking that Autistic people go through every day, and the tiring nature of it and the monumental effects it has on everyone in an Autistic person's life. With this understanding we can cultivate a broader degree of appreciation and acceptance of Autistic people's differences.

## MASKING AND EMPLOYMENT

Through my experience growing up, I lost friends from being myself when I didn't mask, and that's really not my problem, that's theirs. But I know too well that as you try and find your place in the world something comes along that can be far more serious: masking and keeping jobs.

It's one thing to acknowledge the challenges of keeping relationships and masking with your friends and your family because the world and everyone in it is not perfect. Over time hopefully you've found those friends that genuinely like hanging out with you and they understand you to a relationship-level degree. You have fun together, and the same applies if you have found a partner that "gets you" for the most part; they will see and accept all of you at some point because no one can mask all the time. The mere attempt results in some big consequences that we explore in the upcoming chapters.

I want you to gather everything you've learnt so far in this book, and now put an Autistic person in an employment scenario (I will discuss employment and the wider discussion around disclosure in depth soon too).

Jobs are very bound and there are specific obligations to commit to: task orientated, disciplined, big personalities and teamwork dynamics, troubleshooting sudden problems, watching timeframes, meeting deadlines, balancing workloads, and maintaining relationships. These duties and responsibilities can stress anyone, including non-Autistic people, in different ways and levels. Taking our concept of masking and presenting an Autistic person with all these factors, mixed in with a social undercurrent, makes masking in the workplace that much harder.

But even before then, if I didn't mask in a job interview (i.e. present myself to them as a person they would like to hire), I would never get a job. And then if I did get a job, and I didn't mask constantly, I would never keep my job. Now to that I have heard the question, "Well, why don't you just tell them at the start you're Autistic, and then they'll treat you differently?"

And to that I must reply, "Wow! What planet are you living on? I might move to that planet." The reality is, there aren't many employers who will hire you after you tell them that you're Autistic. So in my undiagnosed past I have presented a hireable front through the veil of unknowing masking, and I was then hired and subsequently experienced all the stresses we've talked about, which make constant masking impossible.

My personal experiences as an Autistic adult in the workplace meant I absolutely felt the stresses and pressures from sensory overload, and have then been triggered to have an outburst, unable to control myself any further. I've melted down, I've shut down. Not often, but it only takes one time. I remember in one workplace, over about a three year period, I displayed one meltdown on average each year. One larger-than-usual reaction that was visible only three times in a long period of time.

To an Autistic person, I was actually managing my workload, stress and anxiety pretty well with three years of masking and working hard, to only have three occasions in those years. Yet it was three strikes and you're out. Gone, no job, see you later. The HR department responded to my actions with, "Oh, you can't act like that in a workplace. You can't treat people like that." If I was not Autistic, I guess they would be telling me to behave neurotypically. But as I am Autistic, what they were saying to me was, "You can't be Autistic in this workplace."

Now I'm not talking about behaviour in the workplace that is unlawful or dangerous or otherwise universally inappropriate. No one is above the law. I'm merely suggesting that rather than imposing a blanket and discriminatory ban on Autistic people being themselves in the workplace, maybe we could provide education and insights into autism for the neurotypical employees.

> **If Autistic people are suppressing their true Autistic selves to be included and you think that's okay, you do not understand how inclusion works.**

I'm not giving you an excuse, I'm giving you a legitimate reason behind the challenges of the workplace and the greater toll that masking has for Autistic people in the workplace, both emotionally and from a career and financial point of view.

Further to that, the simple act of empowering yourself with an understanding of autism can change the lives of Autistic people for the better. Improving the quality of life of one person improves the quality of life of another.

## 📢 PICK YOUR BRAIN

I will never understand why people feel the need to say, "Can I pick your brain?" Clearly what they're really asking for is help, assistance or advice, wanting to draw upon your experiences. Okay, so you would like to use my brain. Picking at it won't help. Let's say my kid is busting for the toilet and while we're out, I don't ask the nearest house or shop, "Can I pick your toilet?"

# CHAPTER 9

# AUTISTIC MELTDOWNS

We are really powering through the Autistic world now, but here we are, already halfway through the book and there is still so much to share to lighten your load and shake off those stigmas and inaccuracies around autism.

By now, you're becoming familiar with the everyday triggers, situations and different repercussions that might arise as an Autistic person attempts to manage different scenarios, stimulations and demands in their daily life. But what happens when the anxiety and the masking builds up to unmanageable levels? What is the fallout for the Autistic person and those around them?

The answer is Autistic meltdowns and shutdowns. I want to step you through Autistic meltdowns from an insider's perspective. I'll explain what they are and break down some of the dos and don'ts if you happen to be around an Autistic person in your life when they're experiencing a meltdown.

At some point I'm guessing an Autistic meltdown may have heavily impacted the life of your Autistic loved one, or yourself. This experience is so much harder without having the background and understanding of where it came from and what you're actually witnessing. How would you feel if you had to spend your entire life being someone you are not, in an attempt to be accepted and fit in?

Every single day, an Autistic person is literally trying to live and play by the rules of a neurotypical world: a world that is not built or designed for people born with a brain that diverges from the neurotypical majority. Now that might sound simplistic, however:

> **The mental and physical effects of living in a world that doesn't actually understand and accept us are truly enormous; they're exhausting and cannot possibly be overstated.**

Sometimes, our response to the build-up of these effects over time can be alarming and disconcerting if considered only on a surface level. It's like watching the dramatic end of a movie when you have no connection, emotional investment, understanding or empathy for what the characters have been through. Understanding that an Autistic person has faced many challenges in the lead up to experiencing a meltdown or shutdown is a game changer for everyone involved.

In my opinion, some of society's deep-seated misconceptions have stemmed from the more overt Autistic behaviours that people have witnessed in the past without any knowledge of the individual, the circumstances and importantly the context that has led up to that moment for the Autistic individual.

I'm talking about the assumptions formed solely from what an Autistic meltdown can look like to an observer—"look like" mind you, not what an Autistic meltdown actually is. It might sound strange but the best place for me to start explaining and defining Autistic meltdown is by eliminating what an Autistic meltdown is not.

An Autistic meltdown is not:

- A tantrum. A tantrum is an act of manipulation. It is a physical and emotional "show" to put on to try and get someone to agree to your demands or desires by making them feel uneasy, confronted, confused, embarrassed or threatened by acting overdramatic. A tantrum is controllable; therefore it is not an Autistic meltdown.

- Acting selfishly. This is not a meltdown either. You can't watch someone having an Autistic meltdown and think to yourself, *Stop being so selfish!* They can't "stop" being anything.

- Acting out or attention-seeking behaviour. Again, not a meltdown but can be seen in both adults and children. Autistic children and adults can be susceptible to Autistic meltdowns for their entire life. So the whole only-Autistic-kids-can-have-meltdowns thing is not true. You can't parent or punish Autistic meltdowns out of an Autistic person.

So putting that all together, Autistic meltdowns are not controllable, not intentional. It is an uncontrollable reaction in our brain when it crosses a certain threshold of triggers from environmental, emotional, social, physical (and other) types of overstimulation or understimulation. **It is a physiological stress response that is a sign our brain is in distress.**

It must be understood that reaching this level of distress is okay; it's normal! Autistic meltdowns are our "normal," a natural part of being Autistic. They are tiring and they can be minimised to a certain degree, but they cannot be avoided altogether. The Autistic brain will eventually reach its threshold of trying to process the neurotypical world around it.

If you have an Autistic person in your life, and you're not Autistic, being near them when they're experiencing a meltdown might initially alarm and surprise you. And I get it. Autistic meltdowns can feel and look different for every different Autistic person. To give you an insight however, in general terms Autistic meltdowns *might* look like this:

→ Erratic actions.

→ Pacing.

→ Running or bolting off.

→ Jumping.

→ Stomping.

→ Yelling.

→ Crying.

→ Agitated or angry movements.

→ Lashing out at others.

→ Shutting down, non-speaking, non-responsive.

So Autistic meltdowns can manifest in many ways and behaviours that can fall outside conventionally accepted behaviour. **But behaviour and movements during a meltdown are not consciously controlled or driven by intention to get a result that benefits the Autistic person.** It may be contentious to say but I think some neurotypical people believe we "do" it to get something out of it!

## HOW DO MELTDOWNS FEEL?

So from an external point of view, going forward now you'll have more awareness and sensitivity to recognise when an Autistic person might be experiencing a meltdown. I hope this insight will help activate people's empathy and understanding in that instance.

Let me give you a taste of what an Autistic meltdown feels like for the person experiencing it, or at least, when I experience it. One of the first feelings I have when I first detect what direction things are heading is **a sense of panic.** There is no conscious manipulation of the situation or "decision" being made in terms of how to act or behave; I am not weighing up my environment, not thinking how I can get what I want, I'm not reading the room. I have turned inward. **My heart rate starts to rise,** I feel uneasy, agitated, irritable. I also start to feel fear. It feels like there's no way out, so **I feel trapped.**

I also **feel like a passenger,** and at the time I don't think the ride is ever going to stop. For me, a meltdown causes everything to speed up. My body movements, speech and behaviours become more manic. I tend to aggressively scratch at my scalp, touch and rub my face and neck, and uncontrollably rant. I have also, at times, hit my head with my hand.

On the other hand, shutdowns are just that. I disappear into my shell of a body, unreachable and lost to another world. Self-care becomes a non-existent concern and pure quiet is too loud.

# CAUSES OF AUTISTIC MELTDOWNS

We've been building up your knowledge and resources around autism so some of the causes of Autistic meltdowns will not be a surprise to hear.

Causes, or triggers as I like to call them, can't always be identified. There will always be different triggers for different people. I can't possibly provide you with an exhaustive list, life itself could be on the list! But let's just go through some of the known triggers of Autistic meltdowns, understand how it gets to that point and cross that threshold into brain distress.

## UNDERSTIMULATION OR OVERSTIMULATION

Under the definition of Autistic meltdowns, I talked about the main trigger point for an Autistic meltdown in simple terms being an under or over stimulation that eventually triggers the Autistic brain to have a reaction and experience distress signals.

In practical terms, this concept of crossing a threshold (how much stimulation, or lack of, can an Autistic brain process and at what speed and at what cost?) applies to many key and often daily experiences that you can keep an eye out for from now on. So, what are some of the causes of an Autistic meltdown?

## CHANGE OF ROUTINE

The trusty old ever-reliable sudden change of plans. Ah, that can absolutely trigger an Autistic meltdown. Changes, disruptions and sudden barriers when we're going about our day-today life (the way we need it to be routine-based, with planning and structure); if any of these changes occur unexpectedly they can have a significant and serious impact on an Autistic person.

It is so important to be able to look out for these things. Reading this as a potentially neurotypical person who has an Autistic person in their life means you may well be able to look out for these things from now on by realising, *Oh, I know I've got to change this*. Or maybe, *I think I can mitigate these situations so much more than I do right now for my loved one*.

I know it's not easy, it might even throw a spanner in the works sometimes, but at least you know there are ways to navigate this: you can provide some notice of a change, reschedule, work out other solutions, what aspects can be minimised, and whether it has to happen today. There are work-arounds here.

Not many situations or plans are do-or-die but the world is so crazy busy nowadays, it can seem like we absolutely have to do that silly old thing right now! But sometimes we don't; honestly, we might just need comfort, stability and wellbeing more than anything at all in this world.

As an Autistic guy who's married with two kids, I can tell you sometimes there's just too many demands, too much stress. One of the diagnostic criteria for diagnosing autism centres on coping mechanisms and reactions to daily demands.

> **When the needs, demands and stressors exceed your capacity to deal with them as an Autistic person, you are clearly going to experience some sort of stronger reaction than usual.**

And it will probably be something close to an Autistic meltdown. That is a best-case scenario. You do not want to go into Autistic burnout territory. Trust me. I will explore this soon with you but it comes with more of a "Warning! Keep Out" sign... Or in my case, an "I'm having another nap (yes my fifth of the day), so GO AWAY" sign.

## EXPERIENCING HIGH-LEVEL EMOTIONS

Another big trigger for me before an Autistic meltdown, and in general terms I think others will agree, is experiencing high levels of emotions. Earlier we dispelled the myth that there's no empathy in Autistic people or that we don't feel emotions. In fact, we can be hypersensitive to the emotions of others, and we can certainly feel emotions ourselves at a hyper level. But that isn't the issue.

The issue is expressing them, identifying them, understanding them, dealing with them. So when an Autistic person experiences high levels of emotions and becomes emotionally overwhelmed, and they can't identify those emotions, or express those emotions, it can 100% trigger an Autistic meltdown.

Quite often I can struggle both interpreting the emotions of my wife when she is sharing an experience or story from work and understanding why it is making me feel so strongly. It's not uncommon for me to overreact or be overwhelmed with hyper emotions when my wife shares a confronting or upsetting experience she had that day.

Oh, and who shares an emotional story with someone without wanting reactions, advice and solutions from them? My wife, that's who. In fact, most neurotypical partners apparently like to just "vent" or "debrief." ⟶ *You know you're not in the Air Force, right?*

## LEAVING SAFE SPACES

Leaving our safe space can cause an Autistic meltdown just with that simple act. Remember Autistic people rely on their safe space; it's usually our house, where we spend the majority of our time and have the most chance of feeling comfort and a sense of calm and continuity.

Even though my Autistic son loves the outdoors more than he loves the indoors, it's harder for me to get him outdoors than it is to keep him indoors, which doesn't make any sense. In fact, if you have any suggestions, speak up... they have to be legal obviously. That slowed you down, didn't it? "Oh, precious little Orion wants suggestions that are appropriate, adapted *and* lawful. Well, la-di-dah."

Getting my son to cross the threshold to a place he loves shouldn't be difficult. It doesn't make logical sense to people when you think about it. But it does to me, because I know that he's obviously riddled with anxiety. And also indoors is his safe, comfortable zone. To go outside is a gamble but it pays off every time because it's fresh air, it's sun and it's fun, but you are still exiting your safe space.

Leaving a safe space—forcing someone to regularly leave this safe space—over time can and probably will trigger an Autistic meltdown at some point.

## EXPERIENCING CONFRONTATION

Some of you may have already noticed with Autistic people in your life, certainly a big trigger can be experiencing confrontation. This includes confrontational environments as well that can trigger Autistic meltdowns. While some triggers build up over time before crossing that manageable threshold, confrontation can be different in that it can cause an Autistic meltdown suddenly, almost as soon as the situation is detected.

Clearly confrontational environments speak for themselves, and they provide different triggers for different Autistic people. Regardless of the different triggers, the result of entering or being forced into a confronting environment can have the same result: spontaneous meltdown.

Conversely, I often find confronting people or social situations cause me to shutdown rather than meltdown. In a confronting environment I feel an urgent sense to escape and that triggers a more outward response. However, disappearing into my shell around confronting interactions seems to be my default response. The problem with this response is that it can take me too long to warm up again or feel comfortable enough to come out of shutdown, which has a lasting and negative impact on those interactions.

## 📢 WAITING ROOM SEATING

Let's say you walk into a waiting room, find a chair, and sit down. Then I arrive with my wife and son and we observe there are two empty chairs, one on either side of you. So, my party of three has to split up because you have already sat down in a random chair in the middle.

What I don't understand is that when we arrived and you could see a family split would occur, why then couldn't you move over one seat? You didn't get there early to get the good chair, they're all the same chairs. What? You couldn't possibly move from one chair to another completely identical chair? Oh no, you're waiting, and waiting is hard enough. You can't wait and move; move and wait, for some precious party of three, stretching your legs out so wide that your knees hit people in the next room!?

# CHAPTER 10

# AUTISTIC BURNOUT

Autistic burnout is an intense physical, mental, or emotional exhaustion, which can result in a loss of skills, motivation, or ability to achieve anything. It can be caused by having to navigate a world that is designed for neurotypical people.

Autistic burnout can be confronting for people who don't understand it. The misunderstanding and the lack of acceptance around Autistic burnout can end friendships; it can end relationships; it can affect employment and studying. Yet it is the equivalent of severing a relationship with someone because they had a medical seizure they couldn't control. It's just a severe, unfair outcome that affects so many aspects of an Autistic person's life. Autistic burnout desperately needs to be better understood and accepted in the neurotypical world.

Autistic burnout is the inevitable physical and mental consequence of an Autistic brain trying to live by the rules of a neurotypical world each day. For me, it can be caused by too much masking, which requires a significant amount of effort, energy, and focus. It can also be due to executive function demands like having to juggle too many tasks at once (family and work) and the stress of too many (sudden) changes to your life or daily routine, which is a critical aspect to manage for both Autistic kids and Autistic adults.

Extended periods of time in confronting and overwhelming environments or interactions can also trigger burnout. This extended period can often be as a result of an Autistic person simply trying to please others by pushing past their personal limitations.

In my view, Autistic burnout is when your capacities are exceeded due to stressors and demands that have accumulated over time and you can no longer function like you usually do.

Put differently, your capacity to meet the demands and stressors fails. I've been experiencing Autistic burnout more often as I get older. It could be because the stresses in my life have increased because of the responsibilities I now feel as a husband and father.

But life is like that; everything gets harder after childhood. Not that life is easy for Autistic kids. However, while Autistic burnout is impossible to avoid (every Autistic person will experience burnout), it can be mitigated and better understood and supported by the people who are closely affected when their loved one is experiencing burnout.

Autistic burnout is not a one-size-fits-all experience. Autistic people may experience Autistic burnout daily, weekly, monthly, or maybe only a couple of times a year. For an Autistic person with other co-occurring conditions or chronic conditions, burnout may be more regularly triggered. On the other hand, an Autistic person who only experiences stresses from time to time and not necessarily every day may only experience Autistic burnout occasionally when the stresses eventually build up to unmanageable levels.

## WHAT DOES AUTISTIC BURNOUT FEEL LIKE?

The way burnout manifests can vary from Autistic person to person. I'm drawing on my own personal experiences here but as I feel the effects of burnout in many different ways, I'm going to cover a lot of territory so I'm sure there'll be elements you relate to.

It's interesting that as you learn about Autistic burnout, some of the symptoms can appear as anxiety, or even a deep sadness and depression which can make people think something else is going on, but it's good to look at the whole picture (physically, mentally and emotionally) in case it is actually Autistic burnout. It's a case of learning how it manifests for you or an Autistic individual. These overlaps in symptoms are not uncommon and being aware of what they actually mean can help manage the situation most effectively and sensitively.

In short, during burnout my skills seem to go missing or simply shutdown. My communication decreases, and when I do try to speak, I struggle to find the right words to use. Some of my Autistic traits increase, including stimming, repetitive behaviours, echolalia, and a stronger aversion to routine change and sensory overload. I also struggle to complete tasks I usually perform easily or enjoy doing. My whole life comes to a grinding halt.

## PHYSICAL SYMPTOMS

Let's start with the physical side, which is an intense level of physical exhaustion.

Now I consider my normal state to be always trying to do too much—there's never enough time. Yet burnout will leave me so exhausted I would rather do nothing than do something, even if that something is my favourite activity. I no longer have the ability to "choose," I cannot find the strength to do the things I love and the only viable option I can see through my exhaustion is just sitting on the couch and watching TV or curling up and sleeping.

When I do try and do something or something is asked of me, I can become angry, agitated, anxious or sad more often and I experience more meltdowns and shutdowns. As a parent, carer, partner or family member of an Autistic person, if you see more meltdowns or shutdowns occurring, take this as a clear sign of Autistic burnout in your loved one. They might need attention, support and more understanding than usual. I literally shut down because the world is trying to engage me relentlessly and it has become too much.

> **A shutdown is a brain response where you basically go into uncontrollable behaviour and unreachable places internally, all without conscious intention.**

My brain says, "I'm out." I won't eat or talk; my brain has to reboot. It powers down and will reboot only after sufficient recharge. The burnout is how the rest of you is left feeling while your brain is recharging; all available energy is being sent to the brain for recharging only. No actual normal functions can take place until the recharge has occurred, which can take different periods of time depending on the level of burnout.

Neurotypical people might see what I've just described as a lack of motivation and judge an Autistic person for suddenly having no commitment or dedication to tasks, that they've just checked out and are left thinking they are unreliable. Now you know this is not the case. Their capacities have been exceeded and any plans and expectations need to be accommodated for them to recover from Autistic burnout.

## EMOTIONAL SYMPTOMS

The predominant feeling I have through this intense physical exhaustion is a struggle to manage my emotions. When I'm burned out, it's like the signal or the ability to recognise that emotions are rising (or to understand them at all) has completely gone.

This means they can almost jump out at me (and you), right? Suddenly it's BANG! Anger. BANG! Sadness. BANG! Agitation. Many times during an Autistic burnout period, my wife can say, "You know, you seem really agitated today. Are you okay?" Whereas I didn't even know I was acting that way, but my body language shows her I'm agitated. Or out of nowhere, I'll get really angry or really sad without warning. Whatever filter or gatekeeper I have to be able to function, manage, understand, and interpret all these feelings just seems to have gone away.

Also in periods of Autistic burnout, my anxiety can become heightened to the point where I don't think anything could control it: therapies, medicine, or anything you wanted to try. It gets to the point where the anxiety can't be understood or controlled, and you just can't turn that off. Your nervous system is in override, saying, *I'm in danger*, and when that happens it can exponentially add to the exhaustion.

## INCREASED STIMMING

A big one for me during periods of Autistic burnout is increased stimming and especially using my hair. I like my hair short but when it's been that long period of time where you just can't be stuffed getting that much-needed haircut, it means something to play with, to stim with. Although, play might not be the right description. I'd say more like a firm pulling and picking.

I'll put my fingers through it and pull it up firmly, it's probably more like grabbing or yanking at my hair and would probably hurt someone else if I did it to them. But during Autistic burnout, that is my go-to stimming. I'll be doing that almost constantly, and in some small way, it seems to help me bring myself back, so again, not a bad thing. Well, aside from the fact that it will probably lead to patches of baldness and a permanently damaged scalp.

## REPETITIVE BEHAVIOURS

Repetitive behaviours definitely increase during periods of Autistic burnout. Trying to avoid the sensory overload of the outside world means trying to stick to your routine more than ever. If you're taken out of your comfort zone during periods of Autistic burnout, sensory challenges increase and you'll push back on any idea of having to do anything else other than what you actually need or want to do and in the order things need to be done.

## ECHOLALIA

My tendency to repeat quotes from movies, repeat what people say in silly voices, or sing the same song lyrics over and over again also increases during burnout. I do it to the point where sometimes I think, *You know what? I don't know how to control this.* I can feel the extent of the hold it has over me. I can't explain it but the feeling and sound of the words soothes me. They feel good.

To me, that really annoying or weird voice coming out of me is funny. You may think you're being belittled, made fun of, or attacked, or wonder what that movie quote has to do with this situation. It's almost like I lose my own verbal identity. I kind of become a walking, talking inappropriately odd quote machine. Everything I say is not remotely relevant to what is happening. It is a form of detachment, which protects me from taking in any more stimulation, because there's just no room for it.

## DECREASE IN COMMUNICATION

Burnout awareness will also help you understand a possible reason behind a significant decrease in communication. Sometimes I am only capable of minimal communication, literally talking in short words, grunts and sounds: a clear sign of Autistic burnout.

I struggle to work out the things I want to say. I can feel them in my brain but I can't get them out of my mouth. But it's a self-perpetuating cycle because while I don't really want to talk either, these opposing forces at work impact my emotional control. As communication and interaction challenges are already part of autism, any ability that was left falls away in a burnout, which I feel aware of at some deep level but can't articulate.

To my way of thinking, there is also an undercurrent going on when we decrease communication dramatically. I don't want to talk to people during times of burnout, even my own family or friends, because talking to people contributed to the burnout in the first place. Autistic people for the most part are forced to communicate as a neurotypical person in a neurotypical style to make a neurotypical person feel comfortable.

> Burnout is us tapping out of the match. Our brain says, "Enough; I can't play this exhausting game with its exhausting rules right now."

You can imagine the impact that Autistic burnout can have on your physical and mental health.

## NO LONGER BEING ABLE TO MASK

This brings us to the big one, masking as both a contributor to Autistic burnout, and the fact that you can no longer mask being a symptom of it. It's so important for people who have Autistic people in their life to understand that no longer being able to mask represents something much bigger going on. When you are experiencing Autistic burnout, there's no more ability, energy, motivation, or will left to mask your Autistic self from the outside world.

As someone who has an Autistic person in your life, instead of falling into the trap of saying things like, "Wow, you're way more Autistic than you usually are today," or "She's acting a bit more Autistic than usual, huh?" Remember they have been masking this whole time. You're Autistic or you're not; you can't be a little bit more Autistic than normal. You're just Autistic and then you mask.

This duality is a window into how hard it is to be an Autistic person in the neurotypical world. Our day-to-day life is based on masking, camouflaging, and suppressing our very essence, suppressing who we are as people to fit into a neurotypical world. It is an old, out-dated mentality that thinks Autistic burnout means someone is acting "more" Autistic than usual.

Now we know burnout happens when there is no energy left to mask and therefore the Autistic person is coming across as his or her true self. Which in actual fact, can't be a bad thing...

## LOSS OF EXECUTIVE FUNCTION AND SELF-CARE

On a more immediate level, for me Autistic burnout manifests in a loss of executive function. Completing tasks or doing things that I could usually do easily or willingly, or for pleasure, can be really hard when I'm in a period of Autistic burnout.

There are things you actually still want to achieve, such as basic things for your family like cooking dinner or putting kids to bed. These things might not take a lot of skill but they take effort and I can't find any ability to achieve this. I might wonder what the hell is wrong with me but I still can't do it. This can be debilitating and really deflating. I feel like a failure of a husband and father.

Similarly, memory definitely suffers and I almost never remember anything someone's told me or asked me to do, even if it's something that I want to do. In fact, I don't know if I ever even heard it. A lot of times I find myself saying, "I don't remember that conversation. Really? You asked me to do that?"

Now this is a good opportunity to convey to parents, carers, and partners of Autistic people (including my wife) that when burnout causes us to question conversations or swear that you never told us that, please don't fall into the trap of thinking we are gaslighting you or trying to make you feel stupid. As unbelievable as it may sound to you, we genuinely struggle with short-term memory during periods of burnout. Well, except for my wife, I hear her and just ignore, say 90%.

The other symptom of this disconnect I feel during Autistic burnout is a decrease in self-care. The tasks that are important for someone to do for themselves, I just don't do them; they are neglected or disconnected at a deep level. I don't feel hungry or worry about meals. I don't shower.

*I'm kidding, relax— it's more like 95%. Oh, grow up.*

Seriously, there are so many steps to showering.

Go to the toilet.

Put down the mat.

Turn on the shower and let it warm up.

Get undressed.

Get into the shower.

Alter the temperature for comfort.

Wet my hair.

Wash my hands after wetting my hair as they can get oily.

Shampoo my hair. Wait.

Rinse.

Condition my hair.

Soap up the loofah thingy.

Wash my body in order: chest, shoulders, arms, legs, feet, back, bum.

Rinse body.

Rinse hair.

Wash face.

Rinse eyes.

Final all–over rinse.

Turn off shower.

Get out.

Towel–dry my body in order: face, hair, shoulders, arms, chest, legs, feet, bum, back. Back is always last as drying a wet back uses energy to keep the body warm, therefore resulting in a quick and easy workout.

So you might say, "Why don't you go and take a quick shower?" But a shower to me means 22 tasks that I don't have the energy for. I basically don't do the things you'd expect a grown adult to do. I might forget to drink water all day. No eating, no drinking, no showering. I only go to the toilet when I absolutely have to. I just don't want to contribute to my own care. It's a complete shutdown. In many ways it's like a freeze response.

This is why it's tricky yet super important for not only Autistic people but people who have an Autistic person in their life, to understand the potential lack of self-care that may need support from a loved one. Not eating well, not caring for your body, not exercising, not resting properly, not enjoying anything in your day. While these things can be signs of Autistic burnout, they can also contribute to it as well. Executive function and self-care factors are really important indicators to gauge how well stress is being managed to minimise Autistic burnout. Be aware of this early warning system.

## GETTING OLDER

As I get older, I experience more periods of Autistic burnout. This can relate to also having more stressors, or in my instance having more responsibilities. There are more people in my life that I'm responsible for and care for. That's good of course, but it adds layers of stress. It adds layers of responsibilities. Most importantly, it adds layers of expectations.

As you get older as an Autistic person, you need more time to regulate yourself to avert Autistic burnout. But of course you get less time, right? You get less alone time, less quiet time to do that type of regulation because there are more stressors, more expectations, more demands in your life. Again, that's not a bad thing, that's just a fact.

## STRATEGIES TO RECOVER FROM AUTISTIC BURNOUT

Personally, burnout is a really hard thing to navigate. Like I've said, I'm a husband, I'm a father, I'm an Autistic advocate. I can't just remove myself from life, from the stressors of life. You can't just desert your family and walk away. This is the reality of being an Autistic adult who chooses to have a partner and a family. And I choose that and I want that, and I value that. But I have to realise that along with all those blessings, Autistic burnout is going to happen more often.

So now it's time to get real about strategies that are not only helpful for you as an Autistic person to hopefully avert these burnouts, but you know what? They're actually really helpful, really useful for parents or carers of Autistic children or partners, or friends or family members of Autistic adults. So, listen up.

How do you get out of Autistic burnout? How do you recover?

To put it bluntly, if you can't put yourself in an environment that helps you recover, there's only so much you can do. In order to avoid burnout in the future you need to look at those causes that got you to the point of burnout, and try to remove them or you from those situations or environments.

As a husband and father, I can't just remove myself from my family and go to my fortress of solitude. As burnout seems to occur more frequently and be more difficult to recover from as I get older with increasing stressors, my work and creating content and my advocacy are all things that I can control, therefore they are the first things to go. I have to cut back on output and increase my time doing nothing.

What I also look out for are situations most likely to trigger me and result in burnout. You can avoid full-blown burnout by removing whatever stressors you can from your life or removing yourself from potential stressful environments and situations. Identify the potential stressors coming up each day, week or month and cull them at your discretion.

## STOP SHAMING AUTISTIC PEOPLE

One of the most vocal points in my advocacy is bringing attention to the shame and assumptions that so many people unconsciously place on so many aspects of an Autistic person's actions and behaviours. This is particularly frustrating when I hear the totally unrealistic assumption that someone is suddenly acting "more" Autistic than usual. We know this is not what's happening; it's simply inaccurate.

Let's stop shaming Autistic people for being Autistic. This could well be the most important point I will ever give you. Seriously, it's the easiest thing everyone can do to release some pressure and judgement from Autistic people for reaching the end of their capacities and having a physiological response where they can't continue.

No shame and no judgement is a powerful strategy for averting Autistic burnout in someone you care for.

## GIVE TIME TO REBOOT

During a period of Autistic burnout, an Autistic person's brain reboots or shuts down to recharge. When your computer reboots you need to give it time. You can't use it; you can't continue to demand your computer do the things you want it to do while it is rebooting. There's nothing you can do; you press buttons but there's no response. You have to sit there and wait for it to do its thing until it's back in a functioning state. You may leave, you may stay, but either way, you're not demanding it to do anything.

If you are demanding anything from the Autistic person in your life during a burnout, ask yourself if you treat your computer better than you treat them! Recovering from Autistic burnout takes time. It doesn't just click back on, right? And it requires time and space to be ready to function again. So supporting and enabling an Autistic person in essence to do nothing, to be by themselves, or do the things that they need to do to recharge their lives, to bring themselves back, is actually a really powerful thing to do.

It's an amazing strategy. And it's pretty simple, **if you just let them be.**

## NOT FORCING SOCIALISING

Relating further to that is not forcing an Autistic person into socialising or into activities they might often do. To you, forcing them into these situations might seem incidental, but for someone experiencing Autistic burnout, it's not something that they're capable of doing, and it can also have a really detrimental effect.

So it's super powerful to again, just let them be. For parents or carers of an Autistic child, you may want to consider giving them a break from after school activities and potentially even a break from school if required. Minimising demands placed upon them is also critical. → #demandavoidance

# ENCOURAGE THESE STRATEGIES:

## SELF-CARE

It's important to encourage (and support) the Autistic person in your life to do the things you know will help. Simple ideas are below:

- Provide simple healthy food or snacks that don't take much energy to think about.
- Do some fun exercise together or play a game of their choice.
- Venture outside if they love the sun or rain.
- Run them a bubble bath.

- Have a warm snug towel waiting for them so they feel a soft texture against their skin.
- Read their favourite book.
- Watch their favourite movie together for the hundredth time.
- Ask questions about their favourite subject or special interest.

These actions are positive for mental health as they give the Autistic person a physical anchor that feels good, and they have the bonus of reinforcing relationships. It's so important to encourage these little strategies after the person has had (at a minimum) rest and alone time first.

These strategies can't be *forced*, just encouraged gently and made as enticing as possible from a sensory point of view too.

## GET OUTSIDE

When Superman needs to recover and re-energise, he's got to fly out of the Earth's atmosphere and feel the sun, get close to the sun and absorb the sun's energy on his body. Then he returns even better than before.

This comparison still works for me as an Autistic adult because encouraging outside time to feel the fresh air, feel the sun on our skin like Superman, recharges us and gives us our strength back to be ready again. In saying that, unlike Superman, we are not immune to the sun's radiation, so don't forget to use sun protection when required.

A note of caution: if you just ask, "Do you want to go outside?" this will probably get you a negative response—it doesn't sound worth the energy at all. So sometimes it pays to tackle it subtly using some ingenuity: "Can you see Bluey sleeping in the sunshine outside? Remember how much he makes you giggle when you tickle him, shall we go and tickle his tummy?" The thought of the warm soft dog might just override the inviting nothingness of staying on the couch.

## STIMMING

Again, encourage stimming. It's going to be more intense and more often but that self-stimulation and regulation is going to help the Autistic person in your life in many ways. You don't have to enjoy it. You don't have to be around it, but allow it, foster it, encourage it.

It will bring them back to themselves that much sooner than anything you can do or say.

## SPECIAL INTERESTS

At first, I often lack all motivation to do my special interests and things I love, but I find that soon enough after starting, something small clicks into place and it actually ends up really helping me recover from burnout. If you can encourage the Autistic person in your life and enable them to just go away and do their special interests, their passion projects, that is so beneficial to finding their equilibrium as well.

## SIMPLIFYING TASKS AND RESPONSIBILITIES

Another thing that can really work is simplifying tasks and responsibilities, calling out what does not need to be done. It sounds simple, but while many people find it hard to let go of tasks, the impact of loosening up or rescheduling is so significant, a weight taken off shoulders to let them focus on what they really need in that moment of burnout. Nearly everything else can wait; social media will try and tell you otherwise but honestly, take life slowly and minimise input.

## ALTERING DIET FOR POSITIVE SENSORY RESPONSES

For some Autistic people, it's going to be really helpful if they think about altering their diet during the period of Autistic burnout. I have certain foods that give me a negative sensory response.

So if you can avoid the types of foods you know provide negative sensory responses to the Autistic person in your life, that can actually help them to come out of their Autistic burnout period. If it means eating the same meal three times a day, so be it. Also, I find cutting out the foods that can cause me gastrointestinal discomfort a critical part of recovery. For me, following a FODMAP-style diet is really beneficial. There will be time to indulge again, but why add another layer of discomfort during burnout?

# DEVELOP A DEEP UNDERSTANDING OF YOUR BODY

Now, for Autistic people, I want you to really try and develop a deep understanding of your body and a deep understanding of how your mind interacts with your body. There's no person on the planet better equipped to recognise when you're getting into that ballpark of Autistic burnout.

Get to know your triggers, get to know your stresses, get to know when they are likely to occur and remove yourself from that situation if at all possible. By knowing how they make you feel and by acknowledging those feelings early on, hopefully you can turn it around, or better still avoid Autistic burnout.

Without question, it's a tricky situation but also a very individual one. You will need to ask yourself, *How can I remove myself from stressors and also maintain the life that I need to maintain, which may be a career, a commitment to a partner, to children, to family, to whoever?* It's really a question for you to unravel.

What I do know works regardless of a situation, is to become smarter and more aware about these triggers, so they become your "known triggers," and once you identify them, you can work through them, you can avoid them. Other people in your life will come to recognise them as well and help you in this because triggers can be avoided. It isn't a perfect world, but you can avoid certain triggers in certain situations by thinking about it all beforehand. You just make the decision that's most relevant and appropriate for you.

# UNDERSTAND AND ACCEPT PEOPLE FOR WHO THEY ARE

And the last thing I'll say for parents, carers, partners, family, and friends with Autistic people in their life; the key thing you can do is to understand and accept the Autistic person in your life for who they are. And that goes on to mean letting them be themselves and accepting them for who they are unconditionally. There is no place for shame for being themselves, or anyone being themselves in fact.

I would not wish Autistic burnout on anyone; frankly it's horrible. As an Autistic person, we are literally living and existing in, and playing by the rules of, a neurotypical world that is not built or designed for people with a different brain than the neurotypical majority. That might sound simplistic, but I think the causes of Autistic burnout, although experienced differently, really are rooted in the same idea that we live in a world that doesn't actually understand and accept us yet.

Along with the importance of identifying the causes is recognising the signs and providing strategies to put in place, so we can all have better outcomes and avoid Autistic burnout whenever possible.

# 📣 POST-IT NOTES

Have you heard of those things called post-it notes? They're little bits of paper with an adhesive top so that you can write stuff and stick them somewhere.

Where are we posting them to? What do you mean "post-it notes"? If you're making a note that you can post, you're creating a letter. That's mail. A post-it note is the opposite of a letter. You write a note on a bit of paper and then stick it on some sort of surface where it stays. That's a nowhere note.

"What are you doing?"

"I'm just writing a few go-nowhere notes. You?"

AUTISM FEELS...

# CHAPTER 11

# AUTISM AND PARENTING

My greatest hope in sharing my lived experience and insights as an Autistic person and Autistic parent is to help guide you to effectively change your relationship with the Autistic child (or person) in your life. It sounds ambitious but I know it's possible; in fact it's essential. I can feel your eyes and ears on me hoping you've finally found the difference that will cut through the medical jargon, weight and confusion you feel after exhausting so many avenues that have not made a difference to your life.

I suspect you've read a stack of academia about autism, what is and what isn't autism, what this means and what that means. You've spoken to experts, specialists, and read up on medical models and government reports.

But what good is all that in the moment of actual Autistic experience? What does any of it mean if your daily life still feels peppered with challenges that you can't seem to find a way through? Everyone is stuck on repeat, ending up with implosions—either yours or theirs. You're getting worn down without the hope you thought would emerge eventually.

> **IMPORTANT TIP:**
> There is light at the end of the tunnel because there is no tunnel. You have created the darkness. The tunnel is a manifestation of a basic lack of understanding, appreciation, and acceptance of Autistic people.

Experts and reports talk in general and generic terms to explain brain patterns and behaviours but this becomes rhetorical after a while. Most often, it is totally lacking in the perceptive detail, the action plan, the trigger moment, or well-practised words or gestures that can divert or comfort a person with exactly the right tone or well-timed silence. Feeling ready with some strategies up your sleeve can alleviate those challenging and stressful moments in your parenting relationship with your Autistic child.

I don't have a magic wand to solve all your challenges, but I do have a lifetime of Autistic experiences, struggles and tips to draw on so you have my reality to relate to and ideally learn from in your uniquely beautiful Autistic family life.

# UNDERSTAND THEIR DAY

One of the most important elements to better relationships and more effective parenting is through understanding the reality of your Autistic child or partner's day, be it school or beyond. The following principle can be applied to anyone at any age, it's based on consideration and compassion.

An analogy known as "The Coke Bottle Effect" is, among others, well-known in the Autistic community and rightly so because it's making big breakthroughs in neurotypical understanding in an Autistic person's day. Initially it helped explain to parents of Autistic kids why teachers would say their child had "had a great day," "had no problems at all," when afterwards the child would "explode," dysregulate or even meltdown due to the demands, stressors and need to mask all day.

When the parent checks in with the teacher again to ask if they're sure nothing troubling had happened at school, the teacher is at a loss. Everything was fine from their point of view; they might even infer it must be something happening at home to be causing these issues confronting the parent!

I know many parents of Autistic kids who have borne the thoughtless opinions of other parents and teachers who express doubt their child is Autistic; they don't *believe* the child is Autistic based on what they see. It sounds bizarre writing that, but it happens more than you think. Observers can't see beyond the external layer, beyond the masking, to consider the reality happening behind the young face, behind the child's masking.

Parents of Autistic kids can feel so alone in the challenges they face because no one else sees them.

When other people tell them, "No way, your kid's not Autistic, your kid's smart and empathetic, he can't be Autistic," the Coke Bottle Effect helps explain the misconception between the child's outward behaviour during a specific time period and what is really going on.

If only life were as simple as the teacher's words at the end of a school day. Instead, like a coke bottle being shaken, an Autistic child experiences little moments of stress that build pressure in their minds and bodies throughout the day spent away from their safe people and safe place.

Nothing much seems to happen when the bottle is shaken a little bit but through the course of a school day, the bottle is shaken over and over again. This repeated shaking causes pressure to build up and once the child gets home with their parents or carers, the bottle is opened and you see the true cost of navigating a neurotypical world.

Just because the teacher didn't notice any stressful moments for their Autistic student doesn't mean there weren't any. In fact, most neurotypical people overlook or underestimate the situations that Autistic kids might find stressful and the degree that stress is carried with them through the day, building up to unmanageable levels.

Remember stress is a subjective experience, so something innocuous to you could be monumental to someone else. For example, the teacher thinks getting all but one word correct on a spelling test is fabulous, while the Autistic child can only see that they "failed" something on the test and this adds to the pressure going on within.

Drawing from my own experience, let me get you thinking about the microworld going on in an Autistic child's school day that can "shake the bottle":

Missing out on your usual seat on the bus (shake bottle).

A new bus driver or teacher you weren't expecting (shake bottle).

Sensory noises to process: rowdy classmates, shouting, laughing, teasing, scrapping chairs, lawnmowers (shake bottle).

Finding something unexpected in your lunchbox (shake bottle).

Dropping your favourite snack on the ground (shake bottle).

Feeling hungry (shake bottle).

Being bumped or startled unexpectedly by students (shake bottle).

Incorrect lunch orders, even a tiny difference (shake bottle).

Changes in timetables after planning your day (shake bottle).

Straightening chairs or objects too much and told to stop (shake bottle).

Choosing to not use sensory toys/devices because kids will notice (shake bottle).

Many of the common schoolyard dramas are not on the list for Autistic kids to worry about. It's about trying to deal with the unconscious undercurrents of how the neurotypical world operates that takes up an Autistic child's mental energy. And so, after an entire day of masking, conforming, processing too much stimulation and trying to fit in to rules that don't feel right, when that Autistic child gets back to their safe place with their safe people they can finally be themselves and release all that pent up pressure.

They have to let it out and it has to happen, but it often happens behind closed doors. That's why many parents have to deal with the fact that teachers, parents and other kids question the fact their child is Autistic; they cannot see what we see.

## SAFE PLACE WITH SAFE PEOPLE

I can't stress enough the importance of letting your Autistic child release what (and how) they need to when they come home from their day. Just assuming that means nothing but meltdowns in the lounge room is wrong. Autistic people know what helps them recover, regulate and recharge. And it's not meltdowns, shutdowns or burnout. They are the direct result of not being able to do enough of the things that work to regulate themselves.

For me, alone time, working on my passions (content creation), and zoning out in front of the TV significantly decrease the likelihood of dysregulation. For my Autistic son, allowing him to escape into his gaming world without the demands and expectations of what kids "should" do after school is powerful.

In saying that, sometimes meltdowns are an inevitable part of processing the day.

Imagine their relief when they can finally drop all the acting. It may look like they're "acting out" or "being naughty" but it's all about the extent to which the day has affected and impacted them. The most unhelpful thing for an Autistic child is to have parents, family or friends reacting in unhelpful ways to the release of pressure in their safe place. If they can't do it here, they can't do it anywhere and that would be detrimental for all! It's like taking 10 steps backwards in what you're trying to achieve.

> If they aren't allowed to be themselves in their safe place with their safe people, how can you expect them to think they are accepted by anyone?

The hardest reality of providing this loving environment, this uncensored haven, is that the people they love the most may well be treated the worst or at least witness them at their most vulnerable.

All day long in the real world, an Autistic person has been using all the resources they have within them to:

- Comply with what is asked of them.
- Communicate in the ways asked of them.
- Avoid meltdown.
- Find suitable responses.
- Suppress their real emotions.

- Suppress outbursts.
- Alter the actions or behaviours that are not acceptable to neurotypical people.

After you've been suppressing all this powerful stuff all day, you can only keep it down for so long before it has to come out. So naturally when you return to your safe space, you're free again, you can breathe and it is overpowering, and purely as a by-product, you're going to treat the people you love the most quite poorly because you feel safe with them. In fact, treating others badly is not even the intention; it's the manifestation of masking and suppressing, while being confronted with many triggers of the outside world.

In a neurotypical sense you're treating them badly, however in an Autistic sense, you're not deliberately "treating" them in any conscious way, simply as an Autistic person who's completely burnt out and overwhelmed, who has crossed their threshold of containment.

With the full information at hand, everyone can come to see this outpouring of emotion is not a bad thing; it is not directed at someone, there is no blame being flung around neurotypical style. **The behaviour is a sometimes-uncontrollable release; it is understandable in that precise moment as a consequence of precise circumstances.** Many, many times this behaviour will be inevitable. It's not something they do at the drop of a hat, seeking attention or to manipulate the situation. Even the word "behaviour" is misleading in that it implies a choice is being made. Now you know this is not the case.

**They will be exhausted.** Give them time and space to be in whatever state their brain and body needs to be in to rest; only then will they begin to reset and recover. Gently encourage and enable the things that bring them peace.

Through my own experiences of meltdown and bearing witness to my son's capacities, that's the realisation I've come to. We must allow an Autistic person to release the pent up pressure in any safe and supported way they need to at the end of the day. It's the key to being a successful parent of an Autistic child, to keeping your children happy, healthy and safe, and empowering them to learn and grow and explore.

## PARENTING IN A DIFFERENT WAY

People will tell you that you can't really prepare for having kids. But you think you'll know what to do with the nuts and bolts of it. So my wife and I headed into impending parenthood assuming a bunch of stuff—that we'd parent a certain way based on all our unconscious conditioning and misconceptions we'd picked up along the way so far in life. That's all anyone can do.

I remember the birth of our firstborn son as an extremely joyous time. However, right from the get-go, there were many unexpected challenges he posed for us as new parents. On reflection it was probably the most challenging time of our life. Truth be told, I often feel a sense of trauma, PTSD even, from the experience of raising a young undiagnosed child. However, that is not about our child but more a reflection of the many challenges (and rewards) of parenting a neurodivergent child.

In saying that, I'm sending the therapy bill to him on his 21st.

Fairly early on (well before diagnosis), we realised how challenging it was raising our firstborn son in the standardised parenting model that we'd both been taught. When you're first-time parents you tend to put your trust in the so-called experts that consult with you, be that GPs or Maternal Child Health Nurses.

We soon realised this wasn't working and we would have to parent differently to what we had assumed. The standard disciplinary practices were ineffective and over time we discovered a different brain requires a different disciplinary approach.

> Imagine my shock when I discovered the experts' advice to, "Just let him cry and self soothe" or "Never stay with your child while they go to sleep" was catastrophically inappropriate for a neurodivergent child.

We often felt like punching bags for parents of neurotypical kids who would label our child a brat or simply state, "He just needs some discipline." This advice was especially helpful coming from people with no kids or parenting experience. For those in that category who can't resist the "helpful" comment or two, do me a favour—for the sake of Autistic people and parents, and carers and partners of Autistic people, go ahead and glue your pie hole closed. We don't want or need your advice on raising a child with more differences, challenges and strengths than you will ever care to know or understand.

In the face of the many unsolicited parenting experts, my wife and I worked hard on crafting different ways to parent our child. We devised strategies and ways to parent OUR child effectively. We could get the same result but we couldn't do it in the same way everyone is expected to do it.

A simple example was when our son asked if he could do or have something that we said no to, his response was often pretty intense, even primal. No matter what we said to explain things or how we cajoled him, we just couldn't get him down from that heightened response for hours. You might be asking why, but I can't give you the why. Why does an Autistic brain react like this?

What I can say is that I am prone to catastrophising situations, seeking control to ease anxiety, and melting down when the plan or routine in my head doesn't go according to plan. Even if we changed our minds and said yes to his request, his brain kept having an uncontrolled reaction to the stress of the original answer and situation; the behaviour just couldn't be switched off or made better by any words we spoke.

Any reaction like that was so taxing on his little body too. Now we know these experiences could have been a meltdown, a build up of things that he'd been trying to process without us knowing, and he'd passed his threshold of coping. So, out of our own sense of survival and instinct, my wife and I began to really prioritise what we (and he) needed, in order to enjoy more positive parenting.

If he asked to watch TV, we would look at the parametres of what needed to be achieved overall in a way that could work with some flexible neurodivergent thought. This meant answering, "Yes, you can watch TV—right after you get dressed," or "Right after you brush your teeth." This didn't eliminate the extreme reaction all the time, but it gave him the chance to build up an understanding behind:

> Why can't I watch TV?

> Because you're not dressed yet.

We began to understand that in those early days when he heard us answer with a straight "No," in his mind he heard something like this: "No, you can never watch TV again! It's all over, forget it, shut that idea down now, you're on your own!" It gave him a blanket, hopeless feeling that made him panic thinking that the peace of watching TV was taken from him.

By thinking carefully about our answer and using really factually precise words, explanations and steps, we were creating for him the complete picture of the needs of the moment and the next one. This allowed him to gradually realise if he really wanted something and he'd been told, "Yes you can have it after you do this or that," the clearly described actions became like stepping stones helping him to learn what he needs to do to become an autonomous human being, and also how he can get the down time he instinctively knows he needs.

# AUTISTIC PARENTING

It's remarkable to think that my wife and I were juggling this parenting rollercoaster *before* diagnosis; there was no roadmap, no manual, no useful help or advice that we could find anywhere. All we could do was follow our instincts in regards to what our son needed from us and what we needed from him within reason and within his capacities. We learnt to recognise what these capacities were (didn't always get it right and still don't), and we learnt to adjust our life and parenting technique to them.

Our approach flew in the face of that persistent "old-school" mentality of a strict, unbending parenting model to whip a child into shape, the all-purpose type of discipline that was applied to every kid no matter their character and disposition, to make them conform to conventional neurotypical expectations at all costs. This continues into employment by the way, which is probably why Autistic people are disproportionately unemployed or underemployed compared to all other peers.

If you want to try and tell me it works, you only have to look at the fallout as these kids grow up: the rise in mental illness, turning to drugs and alcohol, the suicides, incarcerations, violence and behavioural repetitions and misconceptions that often stem back to a person's psychological scars from these far less sensitive parenting techniques.

The medical fraternity and society in general now know so much more about the importance of a child's formative years when they are at the mercy of whatever parents, carers and environments they are born into. Each moment has the potential to have a lasting effect on their future wellbeing. While I am endlessly frustrated by painfully slow progress, my advocacy is driven every day by the need to spread understanding about Autistic children's needs, so my son and the Autistic community may flourish as their true selves in a way I never had the opportunity to.

In general terms, the vast majority (well maybe a little less than that) of parents have good intentions to be the best parent they can be. As the reality of parenting hits home, I know how hard putting those good intentions into practice is, especially if there are unique differences and needs not understood by the masses. Add to this the psychological challenge of 21$^{st}$ century parenting dealing with endless dangerous and just plain stupid social media fads doing the rounds each week; it's a massive undertaking for every parent.

At least now I can look back with some self-compassion and understanding that I had the added layer of being undiagnosed myself for the first five years of being a parent. As I stumbled along as a new dad, there were two crucial things missing—a diagnosis for my son and for myself.

Once received however, this opened up a new world of mindfulness and I could look at each aspect and interaction with my son with fresh eyes and a new understanding. It didn't magically make things easy, but it relieved much of the confusion and frustration. Nowadays, **I know what it is we are likely to need at any one time; the frustration comes from not being able to facilitate it due to life's endless obligations!**

# BEING AN AUTISTIC PARENT TO AN AUTISTIC CHILD

As we explore the benefits and challenges of my personal situation, I hope it will shed light on little tricks and tips for the situation you find yourself in in your own life. I'm sharing all this in the hope you might take my experiences and start to recognise a behaviour or body language cue in your loved one and therefore have a good chance of anticipating some helpful dialogue or action you can take to help your Autistic child, partner or friend.

My wife tells me, and I get the impression from others, that I'm not like a "normal" dad. By now I can hear you say, "Well, of course not! You're Autistic," which I appreciate, and I can only present my own parenting experiences from the point of view of being Autistic myself. But there are elements such as compassion and sensitivity that cross all borders and circumstances and those are the things to look out for.

A few factors I believe that set me apart as an Autistic parent are things like being able to play with my kids on their level. I can relate to the games in their head and I can buy into it probably for longer periods than a neurotypical dad could. I intrinsically know how much learning and enjoyment they get out of the game from that moment. It doesn't mean I don't get completely over it as well—who doesn't? "Ah, of course little buddy, I'd love to play the 'nee-naw' (fire and rescue) game again, we've only been playing it since you woke us up at 5am!" There is a fine line sometimes depending on how much gas I have in my own tank.

> The gas usually resides in my gut due to impulse eating.

I'm also naturally hands-on. Now clearly there are neurotypical dads out there who are absolutely hands-on, there's no question about that. But they might have had to make some big mental adjustments to get to the point, whereas for me I already felt like a hands-on dad in the first place so that part wasn't really an issue for me. The reason I highlight that is to help maintain a healthy perspective for myself. Maybe it's just me; maybe it's Autistic people in general, but life has a way of constantly telling me that I'm not good at most things. So reminding myself of what I bring to parenthood helps me to believe I'm not a bad dad. You see, I feel pretty bad at it most days. Many evenings I look back and think how much better I could have done in this or that situation.

I know spending too much time thinking I'm a bad dad doesn't help anyone, so spelling out the things I'm good at is healthy for me and therefore my kids. It doesn't mean I'm perfect and I still struggle most days with not feeling up to it, but I'm there, in the flesh. I'm not abandoning my family so I can go and hang out on a golf course for six hours on a Saturday or hide in my man cave. Seriously, some neurotypical dads get more alone time than me! And I'm the one with the medically diagnosed disability.

# DAY-TO-DAY LIFE AS AN AUTISTIC DAD

Most people write a book after the big finale of their life, after the hardest challenge is overcome and the biggest lessons are supposedly learnt and benefitted from. Well, you can throw that assumption out the window. Day-to-day life is still really hard at times for me, my wife, and the kids too. Make no mistake, raising or living with an Autistic person can be challenging; I liken it to war-like conditions where you are just trying to keep everyone alive. However, living with yourself as an Autistic person starts at birth, ends at death, and is challenging on a level I cannot even measure.

Writing this book is part of my action plan to smooth the way, pave the way for my son as he grows, to know I have tried every way I can to make an impact, and to call for change to as wide an audience on this planet as possible before he and other Autistic people suffer the same traumas many Autistic people like me have endured over the years. Spoiler alert—it's already too late—the trauma of rejection, bullying and discrimination has well and truly begun for him—but I'm not giving up.

It all comes down to letting you in on the details, sharing and providing authentic lived experiences to empower understanding and acceptance of a warts-and-all day in my life as an Autistic parent. It's important to acknowledge that we have two sons; our Autistic son is the eldest. This is not a chapter on how to parent neurotypical children. What it is though, is a book full of lived experiences of parenting two very different boys, one Autistic and the other presumably, potentially, neurotypical.

*At least at the time of publication.*

So my Autistic son is at a very special age, needing validation that I think his ideas are unique, important and heard. But one of the things that I really struggle with is his need for role-playing games. For the most part he can play independently, but the time will inevitably come each day where he must play a game now where, "You will be this person and I will be that person."

He even needs direct participation on the trampoline. You can't just watch him jump. I've got to get on the trampoline with him and play or act out some sort of game. I'm basically like an extra on a movie set directed by my son. What's strange is I have a passion for acting and performing—I even studied it at a legit acting school—yet I experience a fight-or-flight response when asked or made to role-play. Seriously, if there was a union for parents role-playing with their children, we would be taking strike action every week.

So what does an Autistic parent do in this situation? I just do the bloody role-play for as long as I can and then ask my wife to take over. We tag team. In the end marriage is the ultimate wrestling duo. The fight never ends, so you just roll with the punches and tap out when you can. By the way, the fact that you went straight to the bedroom when I compared marriage to a wrestling duo is classic you. Grow up.

Bottom line, I remove all expectations while parenting and do the best I can to remain present and engaged. I find this really taxing by the end of the day but it means my son's had a successful day, playing, engaging, learning and connecting.

# INTERACTING WITH OTHER KIDS VERSUS ADULTS

My Autistic son is not always a fan of playing with other kids. He does play with kids, certainly at school, but he doesn't often seek their company outside of school. If we see someone he knows riding their bike down the street, he doesn't want to join them. So it's all the more challenging that he has an affinity for talking to adults; he walks right up to them on the street and starts talking to them. Usually his opening line is, "What's your name?" These behaviours and experiences are extremely challenging as an Autistic dad. The last thing I ever want to do is call out to someone and start talking to them. It's probably close to the top of my list of the worst things I could do.

Yet, my son loves it, he always has. And he especially does it when he's with me. He'll walk past someone doing something in their own world and wants to know, "What are you doing?" This panics me into thinking, *Dude what are **you** doing!? Can't you see what they're doing? Why are you asking them?*

Short story is I don't want to talk to them. I really, really do not want to talk to them! I have a diagnosed form of social anxiety, so my default setting is to avoid all social interactions, which has turned out well for me given our boys seem to think they are investigative journalists every time we leave the house.

But who am I to discourage such a conversation? Well, I'll tell you who I am. I'm an Autistic person with social anxiety. But the harsh reality is I cannot allow my challenges to inhibit their growth. Each Autistic person seeks connection in their own way, and my son's curiosity and enjoyment to connect and discover is a healthy, positive thing to learn as he moves out into the world one day. And he'd better. He will, right? You know what, I'll just change the locks. You see, these are the paradoxes I face with my own Autistic preferences compared to those of my son.

# TRIGGERING EACH OTHER

On the one hand, as an Autistic person, I can understand my son in a way that most others cannot. I can advocate for my son from actual lived experience and can often discern a rising situation or problem sooner than others.

On the other hand, we are both Autistic and this means we have triggers that challenge us and me being the adult, I must try to mitigate their effects. **However, we do not have the same triggers and can actually trigger each other on a much higher level than neurotypical people would or could.**

My son's words, volume and actions can easily trigger me and I can easily trigger him. It can come across to neurotypical people as though we are willingly, maybe even maliciously, trying to trigger each other! But it's not the case, we don't have the same triggers. And triggers can change over time; they are fluid depending on many factors including stress, environments, situations and circumstances.

For example, as you know, I use stimming in moments I find stressful or uncomfortable. Clearly, if you're an Autistic parent with an Autistic son and a neurotypical son, you're going to be triggered or overwhelmed simply because you're Autistic and it's the real world. And the way I stim, which is often saying really weird catchphrases or talking in weird singsong voices over and over, actually triggers and sets off my son.

> **In seeking to regulate myself I can unintentionally dysregulate my son.**

Usually this manifests in him becoming agitated, heightened and outwardly dysregulated. I'd like to say I always have the insight or capacity to just stop the stimming or echolalia that triggers my son, but most of the time it takes my wife pointing it out and suggesting I leave the room. In my experience, removing myself from his space and allowing both of us to continue stimming and regulating ourselves is far more effective than distraction or trying to stop the stimming.

The irony here is the type of stimming (and echolalia) that I do helps me become a better dad by grounding me amongst the chaos and bringing me back to the moment where I can keep moving and manage what needs to be done as long as I keep those funny voices going.

So the conundrum arises—how can you parent as an Autistic dad to an Autistic son, if your ways of bringing yourself back, soothing yourself and calming yourself down actually trigger the Autistic son you're looking after in the first place? The son who is in fact triggering you, which is causing you to stim, which is causing him to trigger. You see what's happening there? I'm trying to care for him and look after him and in doing that he'll do things that raise my level of anxiety.

For example, my son especially has very little idea of danger and he can put himself in surprisingly dangerous situations, even at home. So my anxiety goes up and then I start to get a little bit agitated, I start stimming, I start triggering him, that triggers me, I do my things to help my trigger, that triggers him more. Next thing you know, fire and gasoline. It's a cycle I am constantly aware of and monitoring. It adds another dimension to parenting that many parents would have no experience with or understanding of.

While I can offer you some advice about learning what triggers your Autistic child in order to minimise or avoid them, it's not something I can do myself without neglecting my responsibility as an adult and parent. I couldn't tell my three-year-old, "Sorry buddy, you're just too loud for me to handle. I've just gotta leave the room for five minutes to reset. Don't choke and die while I'm gone okay? See ya." Not possible.

## SUPPRESSING MY AUTISTIC SELF TO BE A SUCCESSFUL DAD

This brings me to the core challenge of the reality of parenting both my sons responsibly. This means for much of the time I must try and suppress my Autistic self. In other words, I must mask in order to be a parent. I must suppress my Autistic responses, reactions and instincts in order to be a successful dad. It doesn't make me feel good. It saddens me, but at this point in my life I haven't come up with a better way, because I know what providing a safe refuge and welcoming hug and open ears means to an Autistic child and every child.

To parent as an Autistic person is profoundly challenging. Why would I want to spend my day being triggered and potentially melting down and therefore scaring my own children? I would just feel like a bad dad, which I pretty much do every day. It's not like I don't try to be myself naturally when I can, but if I didn't control and suppress my Autistic reactions and responses for the most part, how could I ever parent my kids in a way that would be respectful and appropriate? I'm not sure I could.

If I have an emotional outburst or a meltdown, even though it's an uncontrollable experience, I still understand the effect it can have on people. I don't want my family to feel that effect, so I suppress it. And when I am simply unable to suppress—because no one can mask 24/7—the most effective way to protect my family from experiencing my outburst or meltdown is to remove myself from them for some alone time. My wife plays a critical role in this, as often she can identify my signs of dysregulation before me and takes the initiative to encourage me to have some alone time.

That's the hardest part of being an Autistic parent to an Autistic son. I can see what's going on for both of us and I alleviate and moderate the environment and my behaviour as much as I can for his wellbeing, but I can't always just "suck it up." The idea that anyone can "suck up" their disability is fanciful!

If there were a person who uses a wheelchair and they reached a building that had no ramp, only stairs, would you tell them, "Come on mate, suck it up, just walk up the stairs"? You wouldn't, right? And so, "Come on mate, suck it up, just be a neurotypical dad" is both fanciful and neurologically impossible, given I have an Autistic brain.

# 📢 I'M AFRAID NOT

I don't understand the saying "I'm afraid not."
"Hey, did you get the movie tickets?"

"I'm afraid not." The word "afraid" means, among
other things, that you're frightened, scared,
cowardly, fainthearted, fearful, nervous.

"Did you get the movie tickets?"

"I'm scared not. I cowardly did not. I'm frightened
to answer the question because last time this
happened you broke the house in a literal sense, you
tore it to shreds. I'm scared not."

"Pardon, you're not scared? Did you get the movie
tickets or not?"

"I'm frightened not."

"Did you get the movie tickets?" Yes or no.

No, not.

# CHAPTER 12

# NEURODIVERSE RELATIONSHIPS

Whatever relationship status you are in, whether you are Autistic or in a relationship with an Autistic person, I hope my bare-all perspective on relationships and marriage might just help you avoid making the same mistakes as mine.

Remember, if you are looking for a sentimental, unfailingly positive point of view on how autism is a superpower and a special gift and just plain awesome, then you've come to the wrong place. Or should that be the wrong book? Actually this isn't the wrong book, it's the right book. You know what? Forget it. If you want actual, genuine, lived Autistic experiences that are sometimes less than positive (confronting and offensive even) but always based on live action, then this is for you my friend; read on.

Further, I'll do my best to offer some tips on how you can ease the burden on the people in your life, and hopefully cultivate healthier relationships. I have my wife Dr Renee (or "Hi, I'm Renee and I'm one of the doctors") to thank for a lot of this chapter. Renee is an actual doctor and one of my special interests includes giving her crap about it.

I regularly receive relationship questions from the Autistic community, so my wife and I had the privilege of sitting down to discuss our different perspectives and insights into our relationship. We hope by sharing this honest discussion, we can show you what we have learnt together as a couple and as parents, to assist you and others in the Autistic community going through similar or relatable circumstances.

Many people have asked me what the secret is to cultivating a successful neurodiverse relationship, or if it's even possible! To clear up any confusion, neurodiversity requires more than one brain (person). I am in a neurodiverse relationship because I am neurodivergent (Autistic) and my wife (neurotypical) is not. You don't invest in one stock and say you have a diverse portfolio. That would require at least two investments in very different stocks.

Sometimes Autistic people might think that they can only truly connect with another Autistic person. Not true! Don't just take it from me; let's bring in my other half to give you her take on connection and neurodivergent relationships.

Dr Renee says: *I was always attracted to Orion's humorous, quirky personality, right from the start. I loved the way he would joke around with me. I didn't know some of it was related to being Autistic; it didn't matter. Neurodiversity in relationships shouldn't come into consideration. You either get along with somebody and they support and love you and the connection you have, or you soon realise the connection isn't there.*

So let's assume, you've fallen in love (like me), taken the plunge and committed to a relationship. If one of you is Autistic, the first thing to remember is that this won't change or lessen; **it won't get better because it was never wrong**. This misunderstanding can be the wobbly foundation where many relationships (not just romantic) can unknowingly start. Each person thinks they are being understanding but unconscious assumptions are often expressed in words and behaviour until partners start hurting each other and the relationship dies a slow death of misunderstanding and resentment.

Often, misunderstandings can be caused by the differences between a neurotypical brain versus an Autistic brain conversation. The Autistic person is not going to grow out of their significant struggle to decipher your subtle intentions or inferred meanings or whatever you had in your mind. You know, that indignant reaction, "I gave you mental signals that anyone could have picked up on!" These presumptions won't get the relationship very far. I can't read your body language, let alone your mind.

For neurotypical partners, it's about understanding, respecting, and being generous to the differences of your Autistic partner. Simply understanding and accepting that your Autistic partner processes information differently to you can really help you as a couple. **You're different; embrace your differences.** Even if you didn't know your partner was Autistic when you met them or married them, I guarantee, it was them being them, them being Autistic. All those parts were the things you fell in love with anyway, there just wasn't a label attached to it then.

# A HORRIBLE HUSBAND

So while I have an amazing woman in my corner, I need to confess straight up that I actually think being Autistic can make me feel like a horrible husband. I'm not joking; this is a genuine, real feeling. I feel like a horrible husband because I'm Autistic. In essence, I'm blaming autism for making me a horrible husband.

Let's do a quick disclaimer. Firstly, when quizzed, my wife for the most part, most times of the day, nine times out of ten, I'm 10% positive, does not agree that I'm a horrible husband. Second part of the disclaimer; I, as an Autistic person, tend not to believe a single word anyone says about me if it's a compliment. If you say anything positive about me, I automatically think, "No, that's not true." Perhaps the reality is somewhere in between.

I realise healthy relationships need communication to share feelings, needs, worries and wants. And I accept that notion; theoretically it makes sense. However, one of the main reasons I feel like a horrible husband centres around one of the major challenges of being Autistic: interpreting verbal and nonverbal language. Which pretty much covers communication on every level. I'm also extremely challenged to interpret or acknowledge to myself what I'm feeling, my emotions and my needs—I'm just horrible at those kinds of questions.

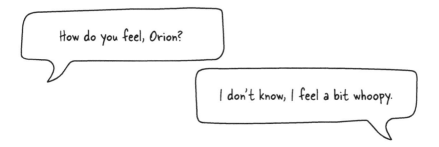

No, I can't tell you what whoopy is. Verbal cues, non-verbal cues, body language, signals, voice tones, facial expressions, and pretty much everything revolving around communication and interaction is a challenge for me as an Autistic person. So you may ask, how do I have a successful relationship at all? The harsh truth is many Autistic people, or any neurodivergent people, don't. My friendship cup does not runneth over.

I tell you, it's from work and effort from both of us every day to be honest. The most worthwhile kind of work there is. The fact is, Autistic people must commit to working just as hard as their partner in cultivating a healthy relationship. Your partner is not your support worker, they are your partner in life.

Throughout the book, you've heard countless examples of how my wife and I can potentially misunderstand or misinterpret situations by not receiving the intended message the other person is trying to convey. So here, we've collected some helpful stories, advice and little hacks to cultivate healthier relationships with the people in your life around the topic of communication and relationships.

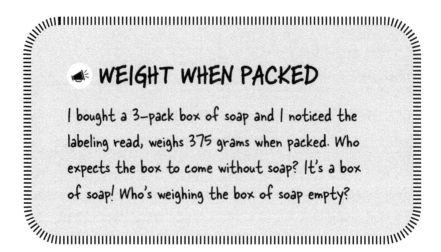

**🔊 WEIGHT WHEN PACKED**

I bought a 3-pack box of soap and I noticed the labeling read, weighs 375 grams when packed. Who expects the box to come without soap? It's a box of soap! Who's weighing the box of soap empty?

# HACKS FOR BETTER COMMUNICATION

We know that miscommunication or a kind of disconnect of communication is a big issue for Autistic people. To begin with, we often need more processing time to work through to the actual intended meaning from our partner, not the meaning we attached to the words themselves. Sometimes our conversations might seem counterproductive; even if they're rational and calm, they still might not go anywhere, or might go the wrong way because I might process it or take it the wrong way, or I might even go on the offensive.

That's why extra processing time is always helpful to work through our different filters first, so we get to the intended meaning. I assume the worst meaning possible when someone is telling me something that has anything to do with me; I tend to catastrophise a situation.

If my wife and I have some sort of disagreement, then I automatically think/believe she is going to leave or divorce me. How could she not? It's all over. It's also important to point out that in a neurodiverse relationship it's actually both people who have interaction and communication issues, not just the Autistic person. Both brains are challenged in their attempts at understanding, processing and accurately conveying the wants, feelings and thoughts of the other person.

Dr Renee says: *Communication in our relationship is about being clear and concise, not too wordy and straight to the point. Before I understood things like I do today, I would get angry about why Orion wasn't doing this or that at home—"You're the one who's been at home, why haven't you put the washing on?" But he doesn't look at something around the house to see it needs doing the same way I do, especially during times of burnout. We had good conversations about it and I'd ask, "How do you want me to tell you?" And he'd literally want me to just tell him what needed to be done. Direct instructions. To stop fluffing around and expecting that he's going to read between the lines. Spell it out.*

*And I think Orion does have a tendency to catastrophise. He'll hear me say something and will only focus on the negative part, or will pull something out and interpret it in a negative way, take it as a personal attack, take it on a completely different path to what I had anticipated the conversation would be.*

*Knowing that he does that helps me try not to use negative language, and I can use his logic and say, "Just hold on a second, that's not the case, think about it. Look at all these logical things about this that go against you saying that I'm going to leave you." Sometimes Orion will say that he's had dreams about me divorcing and leaving him. And I can provide reassurance and proof (often after the supercharged moment has passed) that that's not the case; he's just misinterpreted the conversation or misinterpreted what happened.*

I know I can be distracted very easily. So I try to minimise those distractions when my partner needs to talk to me. You don't have to look them in the eye, but put your phone down, turn the TV or bright lights off, these kinds of things. Make it as comfortable for both of you as you can; this is the reality of putting other things aside, making time for each other and making it work. If you're Autistic and want to be in a relationship with a neurotypical person or anyone for that matter, you can't get your own way all the time just because you're Autistic.

My wife might be upset if I keep looking at my phone while she's talking to me (fair enough), but she never once pulls me up if I'm not looking at her. She understands we process differently and no eye contact is what I need to register what she's saying in the way she needs me to.

Dr Renee says: *One of our key strategies to good communication is that one of us will repeat back what the decision or plan is we've just talked about. Or we'll check that the other person has understood what we're trying to convey. Also, if I notice Orion's body language is reacting in a way I wasn't expecting, I'll check with him if I should repeat it in a different way or ask if what I've said makes sense to him. We are also honest about our feelings and thoughts even if it takes longer to explain things or we process it for a while longer and agree to talk about it again another time.*

# FRONT-LOADING CONVERSATION

For those neurotypical partners out there, when you share your grievances, your problems, your issues, your concerns to your Autistic partner, in my opinion and my experience, it is our one and only goal to listen intently. As soon as humanly possible—as soon as our brain calculates the parameters of what you're explaining—our job is then to provide you with a solution to the problem you've just laid at our door. This "fix it" mentality is absolutely my default setting but it drives my wife nuts.

My psychologist tells me that some people actually just like to talk about their problems and not fix or solve them. They want to use their energy to talk about a problem that can be fixed yet they don't want it to be fixed. Weird but it's a real thing.

So, a super helpful hack for Autistic people is to understand that for the most part, neurotypical people do not want us to fix or solve all their problems every time they share them. Even if it seems they are outright communicating those issues, problems, and grievances to us in order to be fixed, often that's not the case. Our job is just to nod along and make small exclamations at each particularly emphatic point. That is all we have to do! Oh, and at least try and act sincere. Not that I ever "act" sincere.

One of the most helpful strategies my wife and I ↘ *Just* *saying.* have developed in our relationship is something called front-loading conversations. Neurotypical partners, this is key but it's simple. Without front-loading, Autistic people can be consumed with trying to process the meaning behind the words they're hearing and what their role in the conversation is supposed to be. If the speaker adds excess emotion in their voice, my uncertainty rises as does my default setting to "fix" what I'm hearing, so the conversation is fraught with endings that my wife did not want or intend. In other words, you begin to talk to a wall of agitation and indignation on your behalf.

If the desired response is stated beforehand, this can be avoided. Just tell them openly, honestly, "Here's what I think or feel, or need from you right now."

Dr Renee says: *I've definitely found it helpful to open the conversation with something like this, "Orion, I just want to tell you about something that happened at work today and how it made me feel. I don't want you to try and fix this problem." If I need his help with a solution and not just to listen, I tell him that beforehand as well.*

*It's also important to make sure it's the right time for the chat. "Can I chat to you about this or is it not a good time?" Orion might not have the focus right at that moment. And we often have the conversation later when the kids are asleep, after he has regulated from the busy day and we can both talk about stuff without distractions.*

Also for neurotypical partners, it doesn't pay to hint at things. It's not romantic or clever. It just confuses, agitates and frustrates your Autistic partner and therefore you. Sometimes, showing a high level of emotion or feeling to a situation when you're talking to the Autistic person in your life is appropriate and unavoidable; I get it, you need to let it out too.

But many times, it's not necessary or helpful. I know that sounds tough, but I'm saying make a judgement call on how much emotion the situation warrants to be an efficient use of our mental energy. All that emotion you just let out has been taken in by the Autistic person and might squander their mental resources that were better saved for something else. Remember mental energy is a finite thing for everyone, so don't spend it when it's not necessary or helpful in the long run.

## CHOOSING THE COMMUNICATION STYLE THAT SUITS

The hack here (that my wife does so beautifully) is that if there's ever something that she wants to share with me—it could be a positive experience, something that's really angered her, or something she wants to put on my radar to start thinking about— my wife writes a note in the morning for me to find during the day. Or (and I love that she does this a lot) my wife will send me an email. This is a really effective way of communicating with me on many levels. It allows her to be open and honest, and it especially allows me the processing time that I need to add in all my own calculations on the news or situation she wants to share with me.

That's the ideal scenario. Obviously, life often moves faster than that. Daily events spring up at heart-stopping pace and we have to try and use more immediate strategies to get through changes to the routine. This includes asking ourselves what the priority is here, what we can get away with not doing, and whether we can fit in alone time to reset from the setback. Every day is about managing what comes along.

Dr Renee says: *The key thing I've learned with decision-making, especially in the last 12 months, is recognising when Orion is reaching his cognitive capacity, where he actually can't make a decision about something because there are too many factors, or it's impacting on his special interest or particular need at that time. And often, in those situations I'll say, "Don't worry about it, I'll sort it out." I'll keep him in the loop and tell him what I've done without burdening him with extra decisions when I can already see he's struggling.*

*I'll involve Orion in it in a different way without overloading him with all the little details. A good example is with our son's therapy sessions. When they communicated how his session went, I asked Orion, "Do you want me to send you the reports from the session?" And I could see the thought of that made him panic. So giving Orion a summary of what our son has done well and what he needs to work on has been the best way to share that information with him.*

*Also, if I'm at work and I know Orion's had a rough start to the morning, I might text him to check in because I know he probably doesn't want to talk on the phone right then. If he needs to reset, I know having to make small talk or awkward silences on the phone aren't going to help him.*

## ACCEPTING DIFFERENT NEEDS

No doubt one of the toughest points to navigate as a neurodiverse couple has been learning to understand each other's needs and what it takes to meet them. If you're not careful, layers of resentment can build up that erode the foundations of a strong relationship.

If I were to sum up the key things I can do to support my wife, I would need just three words. Showers, shopping and gardening. I do whatever I can to enable Renee to enjoy long uninterrupted showers, and I'm proud to say my current success rate is almost 5%.

*Yep, I'm expecting some sort of medal any day now.*

Renee loves gardening and spending time outside, so on weekends I imprison (sorry that should read entertain) my kids so she can bask in the glow of 15 minutes of alone time outside. Side note, who loves gardening? You get dirty and green and dirty. Really dirty. And the bloody plants die half the time. I've got enough things to keep alive, I don't need plants with a death wish. The last way I support her is… well, questionable. If Renee wants to go to the shops (and by shops I mean to buy more needy plants with a death wish) I never stand in her way—so long as she takes our youngest child. I think we should just move on, but I am expecting another medal.

Having an Autistic partner, my wife has become an expert in supporting and assisting me when my capacities run low; she is an incredible nurturer and very perceptive, a master at reading the room. One of the regular questions I receive from the Autistic community is about the changes in our relationship following my diagnosis. For a lot of people that would be a scary thing, that you signed up for something (marriage) before you knew the whole deal, before there was a label.

In my mind, my wife compromises for me the most and that's why I always feel guilty about it. I guess the guilt comes from a healthy dose of self-loathing and self-hate as an Autistic person. Simply put, Renee is forever bending and reshaping her wants and needs to better fit my needs and challenges.

Dr Renee says: *When I met Orion, I accepted who he was because I felt a connection. The small things were making allowances for how he'd get anxious about travelling. Or he wouldn't sleep very well if something at work was making him anxious, I signed up to that and willingly married Orion for all of him. The diagnosis didn't change those things I already knew about him.*

*The flip side is the same. I'm not comparing the complexity of our conditions but me getting diagnosed with Coeliac disease after we were married actually changed our lives. We just couldn't go out anywhere with my diet restrictions. There are things in life that you get dealt with, and you either continue to love and respect the person; otherwise, the love is conditional.*

*When Orion was diagnosed as Autistic, it was helpful for me to know the "why" behind him becoming overwhelmed in certain situations and environments. Instead of being resentful about not doing certain social things for example, the diagnosis gave me an understanding of what already existed and it has been a really positive step. Especially when I think how he has been able to mask less since then—it's not that he was doing it purposely but rather like getting to know yourself again. He is more comfortable in his own skin and together we have a better understanding of each other.*

## NAVIGATING FAMILY LIFE UNDER STRESS

On a practical relationship level, on one side there's a diagnosis of a disability and on the other there's not. For Autistic partners, how can we lessen the strain of different needs in a relationship, especially when there is added pressure that comes with parenting or perhaps in periods of meltdown or burnout when our capacities are at their lowest? It's a tough and tricky situation.

The first thing I want my wife and others to know is that I absolutely try. Each and every day, I look for the drive and motivation to be the best husband and father I can be. For the most part it works and I feel like a half-good husband and father. Sometimes I try even when I know it feels off; I don't want to leave the house but I still want to try.

Recently I drove into town because I knew we needed some bread and when I arrived I couldn't find a parking space. I drove around the car park again and there were still no spaces. Then suddenly two cars pulled out at the same time and totally discombobulated me; I looped out and literally drove straight home. I achieved nothing and just felt horrible, sad and yuck to the bone. I tried and I failed. There are household responsibilities that sometimes I can't fulfil and I feel ashamed.

At home, we try to split chores but my wife definitely understands in a more direct way what needs doing. If there are chores to be done, I'll do them—but often, they aren't in my awareness, rather than me not wanting to do them. "Who knew there was stuff in the dryer! How long has it been there? Three years?"

Dr Renee says: *It's all about expectations. I don't expect Orion to always recognise if something has to be done because I know he doesn't see the world the same way that I do. It's my responsibility to tell him to do it like we talked about and there's no point in me getting frustrated because I haven't communicated with him.*

*Navigating things well at home also comes down to recognising when he's reaching his level of capacity and how the signs manifest. I notice when he's agitated he does this thing with his hair and I'll be honest and say, "You're doing that thing with your hair, are you okay?" I notice a pattern of behaviour before a meltdown and so I try to use that as an opportunity to circuit break the situation. I'll ask what do you need: do you need to stop talking about something? Do you need a break from the kids to reset? Do you want me to leave the room?*

*As long as it's honest, open communication getting to understand what the other person needs, how they prefer to be communicated with, and how you need to adjust in certain situations. Ultimately sometimes you just have to be honest when the whole day is going to crap and you've had enough and you need time or you're sick of everything—you just need to say that. Stop beating around the bush; if something's not working and it's not right, just be honest with each other. It puts the family back onto an even keel so much quicker.*

## ALONE TIME

Another reason I feel like a horrible husband is my Autistic need for alone time. Without regular periods of alone time to decompress or work on special interests and passions, Autistic people will struggle to function in a neurotypical world. While we can learn strategies and ways around certain challenges to varying degrees, alone time is something that can't be compromised on.

This is a really tough concept from both perspectives. I totally get that age brings more responsibilities. However the concept that just because you are an adult, possibly have kids and you're getting older, you should therefore have to accept there is less prospect of justified alone time, is utterly untenable for an Autistic person.

I would argue til I am out of breath that this just isn't the case. **Alone time actually becomes more required, given the demands in life increase, yet we know an Autistic person's capacities do not.** Our capacity to deal with the extra demands is still right where it always was. It just becomes more challenging with more responsibilities to try and fulfil out of the same bucket of resources you started with.

When I'm unintentionally starved of the alone time that I need, I feel like more of a failure as a husband, a pure failure as a dad. I find it harder to regulate myself. I find it harder to deal with all the different types of sensory stimuli, the sensory overload. It is all much harder to overcome. It's clearly harder as well to mask and camouflage your true Autistic self, which I've said before for the most part you need to do to be a responsible adult in charge of children.

I know that everyone needs alone time, Autistic or not, and not getting enough can create resentment for anyone. It's a challenging situation when I can't always give my wife the alone time she deserves. This knowledge alone increases my stress levels; I can almost resent myself as an Autistic partner. In fact, I do resent and loathe myself.

I know it's a sad fact that this necessity for constant, regular structured alone time can give my wife (or your partner) the impression that we really want to have both; we want to be married, potentially have kids, and we also want the single life. That might be true of a neurotypical guy, but I'm Autistic. I'm not asking for structured alone time so I can do whatever neurotypical guys do with their time to avoid hanging out with their family. I do it because I'm Autistic, and I need to function in this neurotypical world. The big tip here is enough alone time can help facilitate that for your Autistic partner.

Dr Renee says: *Orion often calls it failing, but I don't think it is. I think it's all about the person who isn't neurodivergent resetting their expectations realistically. Life has changed since we had kids, and yes, some resentment initially came to the fore after parenthood but mostly because of misunderstanding the core principle that for him to remain regulated, he needs alone time that is away from the kids, away from me, away from all the other stimulants in the environment.*

*While I'd love to go out to the garden more or the beach, there are always kids' things that need doing, things for the family. It's about realising that I do get alone time but it comes in different forms to what it used to. I might take longer showers, getting time by myself. Or I take* longer *when I'm out than I have to, I'll drive the long way home.*

Again with the gardening! You see what i'm dealing with here?

# RESPECTING DIFFERENT OPINIONS

This next reason that makes me feel like I'm a horrible husband is not that uncommon to Autistic people in my experience. As an Autistic person, do people ever tell you that you are always arguing? That everything they say is wrong to you? That you're always correcting them? Does any of that sound familiar?

Let's talk about respecting differences. As an Autistic person, it's my experience that I often find it really difficult to understand or accept differing thoughts or opinions. I'm aware this sounds odd but I honestly struggle to process, understand, and accept differing thoughts and opinions to mine. It is also not uncommon for Autistic people to see any opposing viewpoint as a direct attack, which clearly requires a counterattack.

I can also have a sense (again this is an insight into me personally and is obviously not true) that my brain has access to all the answers and all the solutions. Just like I can listen to an issue my wife has and quickly provide the perfect solution, and so I am sorely tempted to jump in and provide the answer to anyone that has posed a "problem" in any conversation. The answer rings out in my head clear as day; how can everyone not see it?

However, I know I do not have all the answers, I know this is not true. Autistic people, I know it feels this way but it's not true. Sure, sometimes we have an answer, but we don't have all the answers and all the solutions all the time. We shouldn't just cut people off because we think "we've got it" based on whatever algorithms of thought we have. So the critical thing for me to remember here is that my black-and-white, logical way of viewing the world could actually have a detrimental effect on my wife, in the respect that because of my steadfast answer she can think that her opinion and her thoughts don't count.

However again, I absolutely know that is not true, but Autistic people must acknowledge the effect our approach can have. The issue for me is that I can't just turn off my brain or turn off the way my brain views the world.

> **I can't turn off the fact that an Autistic brain has a stronger logical side than emotional side.**

Side note: even to this day, it is still my experience that the wider community not only wants but expects Autistic people to flick the switch and turn off their autism when in the presence of neurotypical people.

So some helpful tips about respecting differences is to learn and understand as much as you can about yourself first, including what traits and tendencies can occur if you are Autistic. The same applies in general about becoming more self-aware for everyone. Then, with this knowledge, try and be as open as you can, getting the timing right to have conversations and discussions with your neurotypical partner with respect and a generous attitude.

Now by saying that, it reinforces to me that I'm a horrible husband. If I need to tell myself I should be respectful and generous to my own wife, I'm a horrible husband, right? Do you see what I'm saying? This is why you can argue all you want that I'm not a horrible husband but I've just shown you how I am.

Dr Renee says: *I actually love hearing different opinions and different ways of thinking about things because it challenges me mentally and cognitively as well, which is healthy to be challenged. I don't always agree with Orion's opinion, but there's always something I can learn from considering different points of view. I always know that I'm going to get the absolute, 100% honest answer if I ask Orion or Conan (our Autistic son) a question. It can come across a bit harsh if you don't understand the wider context but I value that honesty.*

# INTIMACY

I've always had a complicated, confusing relationship with intimacy and this is the next reason why I think being Autistic can make me a horrible husband. In effect, one minute I'm cool with touch, touching and being touched, and the next minute, I'm deeply startled and brush it off as if it were a deadly spider. In fact, any creepy crawly for that matter.

So I realise this is a hard thing to anticipate and manage. One moment it's okay for me to feel their arms around me or a hand on my leg in connection. And it could be a minute or an hour later, they try to do the same thing and I react with "Get off me!" Clearly these types of actions and reactions as an Autistic husband can give my wife the impression that I am being cold, uncaring, or lacking compassion. And potentially even worse than that, I'm simply disinterested or no longer interested in my wife, which is absolutely not the case! She is my best friend, soulmate, lover, advocate, and partner in life.

However, in the course of me being me, this type of reaction in general can affect more than just my role as husband. If I were to ask, "Hey guys, what do you think of me?" You'd be within reason to answer, "Well, you're pretty cold, uncaring, and you don't really seem that interested in us. I mean, it's like you're magnetically opposed to being near us." It's not a good sign for forging and maintaining relationships of any sort.

What I've also failed to understand and acknowledge as an Autistic person is that physical closeness is just one form of intimacy. See, to me, when you say intimacy, I think sex, right? Sex equals being intimate. Turns out (not that I knew this) intimacy can be verbal, emotional, spiritual and expressed through the doing of things for your partner.

Yeah, I cut the grass. Intimate.

# HACKS FOR BETTER INTIMACY IN RELATIONSHIPS

Okay, so some helpful hacks on intimacy for the non-Autistic partners in these relationships is to model or show your Autistic partner other forms of intimacy that you appreciate.

I also think it's important for neurotypical partners to have open honest conversations about sexual desire and sexual activity. Honestly, this shouldn't be an uncomfortable thing. Just be open and honest. When it comes to sex, you have to be really clear when, as a neurotypical partner, you're simply not in the mood or not interested in some sort of physical activity; just be clear but gentle as well. Autistic people can be really sensitive to any kind of criticism or negative feedback. And when you say no, we automatically think you don't like us anymore, or you don't love us or want us anymore.

Dr Renee says: *Intimacy is sometimes about what your body language is showing and vice versa but often I have to be blatantly obvious and just say what I want. Don't expect the other person to know what you're thinking. One of the successes of our relationship is the fact we are honest and upfront.*

# FRIENDS AND SOCIALISING

This reason why, as an Autistic person, I think I'm just a horrible husband is a big one: it's occurred to me that since we met, my wife has slowly lost touch with most of her friends. Now in life, I know this isn't unusual for friends to drop away or move away, and new friends to come in.

So while I don't think it's specific to our relationship alone, it's certainly something that lives in my brain in terms of the role I've played in these particular circumstances for my wife. I sometimes ask myself: since we met (since my wife met an Autistic partner), where have her friends gone? I feel like this could be my fault.

As an Autistic person, I prefer alone time over the company of others. Social settings cause increased levels of anxiety and stress; it's just a default setting in my brain. I'm not usually interested in meeting or making friends. I seem to find them or collect them along the way just through doing things in life that I have to do at this age and situation. Don't get me wrong, I value friendships; however, it is the finding, making and maintaining parts that are especially challenging for neurodivergent people. And at this stage in my life, my family unit is filling a once-large void.

My wife naturally has a default preference for looking for socialising, and the opportunity to meet people and to connect. It makes sense as it's a standard neurotypical feeling, so it's important to me that she can still fulfil this. We talk about it honestly and see how we can make it work unconventionally sometimes.

## HACKS AROUND FRIENDS

Autistic people, if you're like me, don't go looking for new friends; you don't like socialising because it's stressful, and that's okay—no one should force you into those situations. But your aversion doesn't mean that you have to push that upon the neurotypical partner or people in your life. Socialising is important to them. If they suggest some sort of social gathering, meet up or catch up and your Autistic brain automatically emits darkness and negativity, your partner is probably not going to go through with it because they've got the impression loud and clear that you think it's a horrible idea.

Try going about it a little more like, "Well, it doesn't sound like something I'd be too comfortable doing, but I really think you should go. I'm happy to hang out with the kids, I'm happy to not go, it doesn't bother me. I won't be offended, I think you should go." Full disclosure, I have a two percent strike rate at successfully conveying this to my wife.

Encouraging and enabling your neurotypical partner into those situations, rather than just spewing out negativity based on your preferences (which I'm told we all do sometimes), I think is really important to consider. A neurotypical partner can come across sometimes as like a quasi-support worker. Therefore it's critical that the neurotypical person in your life has a good support network, a good body of friends, a circle they can rely on, to debrief, talk, share, and discuss how their life's going.

And for neurotypical partners, it's pretty straightforward that you need to understand and accept that you're not going to be able to change your Autistic partner (I'm sure at least ten percent of you don't want to) or make them or guilt them into doing the kind of social things or the outings that you want to do.

It's understandable to encourage and sometimes "push" them to do things with the family and extended family; I respect that. But you know what? If there are things you want to do, I think you should just do them. It's not like a divorce or a breakup; you're just going to a barbecue, or a party, or a friend's house, or a cafe. I mean, you're coming back, right? You are coming back? Tell me you're coming back!

Dr Renee says: *Socially, it's about working together to compromise on what we both want. If there's no chance that Orion wants to go to something that I really want to go to, we'll talk about it and I'll maybe go for two or three hours, he'll look after the kids and I'll relax with friends for a while. We talk honestly about what is and isn't possible for us. I look at all the other great things that come from our relationship and how much support he gives me in other ways, and I don't get stuck on what isn't possible. I also work five days a week and interact with a lot of people so I get my cup filled socially at work as well. I don't need to catch up with people socially on the weekend; I love that family time.*

And by love she means for the first 15 minutes on a Saturday.

## SPECIAL INTERESTS

Something important to remember if your Autistic person needs to spend time doing their special interest or passion, whether you are a parent of an Autistic child or a partner of an Autistic person: you can find that these special interests can isolate them from you and the family. Often their special interests are by themselves, working on something alone or sometimes with people who aren't their family.

As a result, in my case, my passion potentially isolates my partner and my kids. I don't always realise this, but I can acknowledge that what I'm doing right now (writing this book) is my special passion and interest and there's no one else in the room as I do this. My family is downstairs, playing and hanging out. I constantly appreciate and I thank my wife for allowing me to do this. However, for Autistic people, it's important to understand that our passions and alone time can isolate and impact the family members individually and as a unit.

Dr Renee says: *It's important for neurotypical people to understand that it's not the intention of Autistic people to make you feel isolated or abandoned. Don't take it personally, because it is absolutely not about you. It's purely one of the main ways Orion regulates himself, through spending time on his special interest. On the one hand he is doing it for himself, but on the other hand the net result of protected special interest time is mutually beneficial for our family as Orion is able to regulate and recharge.*

# LATENESS

Another reason that might sound weird at first as to why I feel like a horrible husband is related to the topic of lateness. Now, as an Autistic person (you might already know this), you can potentially be a little bit of a stickler with regards to time, rules and routine.

As Autistic people, we rely on rituals and routine. We rely on carefully planned-out days as a way of regulating ourselves and trying to thrive in a neurotypical world. So if my wife leaves for work in the morning a bit late, or gets home from work in the afternoon a bit late, it can throw my entire day into disarray. Same for activities—if my wife says a particular activity or an outing will take a certain amount of time and it takes longer, I actually feel a natural sense of anger. In other words, I'm disproportionately affected.

In my experience as an Autistic person, I can really struggle to understand time pressures and constraints concerning things that I'm not involved with. If it's work and getting home, or an activity that I'm not doing and you breach the time constraints, I don't—I can't—understand it because I wasn't part of that situation.

See, if I were part of it, it wouldn't matter. If it were traffic, I could see there was an accident. Or if you needed to get extra ingredients and I was with you, I could see why it was taking longer. But if I'm not part of it, my brain struggles to understand it. And it's just like, "Well, what's wrong with you? You can't drive straight home? Why does it take so long? I can do it in 5 minutes. Why does it take you 10!?" Right? I cannot process or accept the lateness to the routine if I'm not actually involved in that particular activity or time constraint.

## HACKS FOR LATENESS

So some helpful hacks to help you cultivate healthier relationships with the people in your life around the topic of lateness is to be aware that your Autistic partner may in fact get angry or react disproportionately to what would be expected if you arrive home later than usual, or if you take longer than expected in a particular activity (even by mere minutes).

Dr Renee says: *Try agreeing on less rigid times, or use specific timeframes instead. So, I may tell Orion that this is going to take me 15 to 20 minutes, or I'll be home between 5pm and 5:30pm. If you can foresee that you are going to be late or take longer, update the plan as soon as you suspect this is the case: "I know I am going to be late home from work, I should be home between 6pm and 6:30pm" or, "You know what, this salad is more complicated than I thought, it's probably going to take 15 to 20 minutes." The simple act of providing an update absolutely helps.*

## 📣 WORK CUT OUT FOR YOU

Why, when you have some really hard work in front of you, do people say, "Well, I've really got my work cut out for me"? If it's so hard, why is it already cut out for you? They've taken your work that's apparently hard, they've cut it out, pre-planned it, it's ready to do!

AUTISM FEELS...

# CHAPTER 13

# DEMAND AVOIDANCE

L ife can feel tougher than you are sometimes. This book is all about making a difference when you find yourself struggling in one of those difficult and never-ending daily challenges as you try to accomplish the necessary routines of life. I want to help you when you're going through those really tough moments.

When you're thinking, *Oh my God, I'm going crazy. What's going on? How do I parent this? How do I get through this?* Or perhaps on a more personal level you're asking yourself, *Why do I do this if it drives my partner mad? Why can't I do what is asked or expected of me at certain times?*

Let's talk about something very real and very misunderstood by most people: demand avoidance and autism. While I'm referring to demand avoidance and its connection with autism, there is also a clinical form known as Pathological Demand

Avoidance, or PDA. In my experience, a lot of Autistic people who might not meet the criteria of PDA absolutely experience a level of subclinical demand avoidance that plays into their lives and relationships with their loved ones. It's another long-overdue topic that should have been discussed decades ago but is only now being recognised for what it is.

In simple terms, demand avoidance is when you find yourself unable to perform a task at a particular and necessary time and the main driver behind why you can't do that task is because a demand has been verbally expressed or reiterated by someone for you to do it. Demand avoidance is basically an obsessional need to resist or avoid sudden or emphasised demands, which can lead to sensory overload, meltdowns, aggressive outbursts, and burnout.

It's not that you don't want to do that task/job/chore (whatever form the task comes in, even something fun), it's that an intervening demand to do the thing "now" or very soon has rendered you unable to do it. Your brain is unable to face or engage in the task. It's like a heavy weight has been placed on your head, making you unable to physically move towards the objective.

## DEMAND AVOIDANCE IS NOT A CHOICE

Without even knowing the research, as an Autistic person I've always struggled with demand avoidance. Learning about the psychology behind demand avoidance was both eye-opening and a relief in understanding that demand avoidance isn't actually a choice for Autistic people. **It is not a tantrum, it is not an attempt to manipulate, and it is not an attempt to shirk responsibility.** I know there can still be brat behaviour and throwing tantrums and just not doing things because you don't want to. You can learn to tell the difference between these situations; one is intentionally motivated or manipulated, the other is absolutely not.

Demand avoidance is not something we just decide we feel like doing or not doing. It shouldn't be treated like a tantrum; it is the manifestation of a disability. This condition should and must be respected, just like any other manifestation of any other disability.

I know it can be a tough perspective to understand for the non-Autistic person who is watching the external results of what's going on inside for the Autistic person. A parent, carer, friend, family member or partner of an Autistic person may fall into the trap of belittling and disparaging what looks like certain chosen "behaviours." It looks like you're having a tantrum or acting like a child. However, the resistance to the demand you are seeing is actually akin to an impenetrable mental wall.

It is so important to acknowledge that this is a condition and you need to look out for the signs. I have plenty of everyday life examples that will resonate with you. For example, starting off simply, sometimes when there is something I am going to do and I have even planned to do it, but before I actually start doing it someone intervenes and *asks* me to do it, and like a switch being flicked, a wall goes up. I can't see past it and now I can't do the thing. The intervening act of asking or reminding has now rendered me unable to do that task, the very task I'd planned and wanted to do—I tell you, this is not a choice.

From another perspective, demand avoidance can arise for me when other people are relying on me to do a particular thing or task.

> **The sense of someone's reliance on me can actually cause me to be mentally unable to complete that task. Not unwilling, unable.**

Another more specific example is if there's something that I want to do but a time constraint is placed upon it, I am unable to do that task. The time constraint has totally overshadowed any desire or fulfilment I would have felt from the task had it been free from any constraints.

Let's take my favourite thing to do: create content. This lights my fire and I could do it all day, every day, and my wife knows this. So when she notices (very occasionally) that a window of time has opened up unexpectedly in our day, she is the picture of magnanimity and offers this window up to me, "Why don't you go and do a video?" Yeah, why don't I?

Because! Knowing how long videos actually take to set up, prepare, record, edit (yes, all the fun stuff I love) and now I have to add in a time constraint that's been placed on me, therefore the whole proposal becomes unacceptable to me; my brain does not compute that it is possible or would be enjoyable in any way. No doubt to my wife it sounds like I've just "chosen" not to do it and that I'm having a little tantrum, being a big brat, and that I will only accept the perfect conditions in which to indulge my passion.

But no, it is the creation of a very set situation that causes anxiety and kills any creativity I may have had going into it. Nowadays, my wife totally gets it; she gets me, but it's taken a long time to get to that understanding together. From my point of view, I find it hard to convey to people the complexity of demand avoidance in a way they can believe it's not a tantrum. In no way am I simply declaring, "No, I just won't do it in that time constraint, forget it," and trying to make some sort of point. Rather it's a genuine feeling; an inability to start that task, knowing there's a time constraint ticking away that becomes louder than my thoughts.

If you have found yourself in a similar situation (either my perspective or as a partner) there has probably been push back in a way that seems like an ungrateful tantrum, a "mood." But it's because up here in the brain, an immovable barrier appears and renders me unable and physically incapable of moving towards the task.

It may surprise you that personally, I don't think I consistently meet the criteria of a diagnosable form of PDA. I would say my experience of demand avoidance is more transient. When the stimuli around me are at a minimum, demand avoidance is not always an issue. I find when I'm in extended periods of overstimulated environments or periods of shutdown or meltdown, those already heightened states can trigger demand avoidance to manifest more often and certainly in periods of burnout it will occur more often. And similarly regular experiences of demand avoidance can take its toll mentally and itself can lead to burnout.

# EXAMPLES OF DEMAND AVOIDANCE IN ACTION

The number one example of demand avoidance for me was studying at law school. Have I told you that I dropped out? I can tell you one of the main drivers for me being unable to continue in that study environment as an Autistic person was demand avoidance.

At university, it's very important to contribute to tutorials, where small groups get together and talk about the content for the week, and your participation is part of your assessment. "Attendance is only 10% and participation is the rest," blah, blah, blah. You are *forced* to contribute to tutorials. This absolutely triggered me and just filled me with immense dread and anxiety and almost shut me down. Even if I knew the answers, I couldn't contribute because I was being forced to contribute. I know how contrary this sounds but I can only provide you with my own personal experiences.

Another law school trigger of demand avoidance for me was the obvious, the classic, the lecturer asking questions by pointing at people and singling them out to spiel off their witty answer without skipping a beat. Every assessment—essays, written pieces, research projects, or whatever form the assessment came in—stipulated word counts. So the idea that I had to stick to a strict word count and submit the assessment by 5pm on a precise day, I could feel the weight of the time constraint on me from the moment I received the assignment.

Demand avoidance is one of the main reasons why I try to avoid appointments. I try to avoid making commitments to travel to different places to meet people. I realise they don't place the demand on me to make an appointment in the first place but once it's made, there is a demand on me that I must fulfil, at both a certain time and most annoyingly a certain (usually unfamiliar) place.

I could travel all over the world on a holiday, but it's on my own terms. I have the support of my wife and can maintain routines and preferences. It's strange. I get it. It doesn't mean I don't go to appointments, it just means it's something I genuinely struggle with. I will always try to book my appointments in the morning because—and I understand this may seem silly—I will often struggle to do anything else prior to an appointment. The anxiety and demand of appointments often lead to an incapacity to achieve anything but the appointment itself, my lone achievement for the day. It is often about finding the balance between what's necessary and what you're capable of, and even between what you want to do and what you can do.

Despite loving everything related to content, YouTube and podcasts, demand avoidance can absolutely lead me to have long periods of time where I simply can't work or create content because I feel like there's some sort of demand placed upon me.

In these instances, even though I love it and I want to do it, I just can't do it.

It can seem even stranger therefore to people who don't understand or experience this that despite wrestling with demand avoidance and not working on content for days on end, I can, however, spend hours working or doing other things that have no demands or deadlines placed on them. Like spending four hours going through family photos to make a calendar, even though it wouldn't be used for six months. These little unplanned alternatives (based on any idea that has popped into my head with no real goal or timeframe or deadline) are no worries at all.

With anything that is time sensitive, I am absolutely going to struggle. Someone might say to me, "Hey, can you do a podcast? We want to put it out next week." This might be a really great idea, but my mind automatically creates an alternative task that

I'd much rather do—"I know! Let's start a new channel where I just make videos of me hiding behind doors and scaring my family. Let's go!"

My wife's favourite, I'm certain, is if she reminds me or asks me to do particular chores—maybe wash or fold some clothes, go to the post office, go to the shops, do this, do that. Something inside me rises up and I cannot prioritise that right in that moment. This is the hardest bit to convey. It's not because I don't want to do what people ask me. When no one mentions it and I can see for myself that there's a big pile of washing or some parcels need picking up, I just go and do them. No demand avoidance in sight.

# 10 TIPS HOW TO BEAT DEMAND AVOIDANCE

I hear you say, "That's all great to know Orion, but how do we manage it? How do we get around it?" Here are my top tips for both parents and carers of Autistic children and for the partners of Autistic adults.

### TIP #1:

Firstly, is it demand avoidance? As a parent or carer, you'll become finely tuned to determine if your child's actions, words and body language are signalling demand avoidance or not. Is the resistance a type of moody manipulation to avoid a responsibility they just can't be bothered doing? Or are they showing relentless push back and rising anxiety to the demand?

Only you can learn the individual patterns and tendencies of the child in your care.

## TIP #2:

Once you recognise demand avoidance when it's happening, I would strongly recommend not minimising or downplaying it in any way. While you're observing their psychological and physical resistance to the demand, refrain from saying things like, "Oh, for goodness sake, just get on with it, would you? Make it happen! Snap out of it!" Autistic people experiencing demand avoidance can't actually do any of those things.

Don't beat yourself up either if you are Autistic. You can't just "get on with it"; in that moment you are experiencing a condition that you were born with that exhibits under certain circumstances. I'll tell you something that *is* up to you though: learning to understand your triggers around demand avoidance and putting in place self-care strategies to work around when this happens. Having open communication channels with those you live with is also really important.

By saying all those things around "just do it," you are adding additional layers of demand. The Autistic person is already unable to meet the demand; the pressure has effectively shut down their brain to that task. And so continuing on this insistent trajectory is not helpful for anyone.

Look at it like this. You've heard it before but the semblance is positively true. Telling an Autistic person experiencing demand avoidance to "just get on with it" in my view is the equivalent of telling a person who uses a wheelchair to just walk up the stairs, "Come on, just get up. Enough of this, walk up the stairs." In both instances we are talking about a characteristic of a medically diagnosed disability. Let's get past this.

### TIP #3:

A big tip to beat demand avoidance is advance notice. This is pretty simple. People who experience demand avoidance benefit from knowing what's going to happen. So anything from giving them a quick heads up or even providing them with a clear understanding of what's going to happen at upcoming events is so important and so critical.

And so you ask, "Why is that Orion?"

I'll tell you why: it gives them a sense of control. If you have a sense of control, as in, "I know what's coming up today or this week, I know what's going to happen, I know how it's going to play out," you feel like you are in control and therefore, you are less anxious and more comfortable. And importantly you are more willing to do things that you would never have done if they were suddenly placed upon you. Demand avoidance and anxiety are pretty much interconnected.

So don't look at it like a tantrum or being lazy or controlling, it's beyond all of that. Remember, panic and anxiety are felt or seen once the feeling of control is already lost. The Autistic person does not feel in control at all once the demand is placed on them; **you are witnessing the panic from loss of control.**

An added bonus for advanced notice and advanced time is that it provides an Autistic person in your life with more of the required processing time to get their head around what's coming up, which is always a good thing.

**TIP #4:**

The next strategy you can use to beat demand avoidance is to stay calm. This might sound pretty obvious but from my experience and talking extensively with the Autistic community over so many years, I think most people do not manage to stay calm in the face of witnessing demand avoidance.

When the Autistic person in your life becomes anxious or starts to panic as a result of a demand placed upon them, hand on heart, can you tell me you never go near matching their energy? Bottom line is we need to stay calm. So for me, if it's my Autistic son (or my wife, if it's me) we don't want to match that energy. It's not the right sort of energy to be escalating.

For the Autistic person, there can just be panic. There can be a panic attack. There can be outbursts. There can be anxiety. It can be very easy to rise to that energy, but it's very important to stay calm in that scenario. Your calmness is like the ground under their feet that they rely on. They will start to recognise it, feel it and respond to it, if left alone and given time. So don't fall into the trap of matching their energy; it can lead to a larger, more prolonged experience. By staying calm in the face of their anxiety, you're in effect helping them overcome that anxiety.

**TIP #5:**

This is a big one and has a few adaptations for you to try. Once you get the hang of this tip it will become your best friend, your go-to thought process before you even open your mouth! I'm sure we can agree by now that directly asking the Autistic person in your life to do something can trigger demand avoidance. Newsflash! Forget the direct approach.

My wife and I have learnt the incredible effect of using indirect language. Telling my Autistic son, "Brush your teeth," doesn't work. Even if we go for the solidarity angle—"Everyone brushes their teeth, mate. No one wants to do it; we all have to do it. Just brush your teeth"—this won't work either.

Instead, we have learnt the benefit of giving more of a sideways context behind why things need to be done. When there's an issue, we use something along the line of, "Hey buddy, brushing your teeth keeps your teeth and gums clean and your mouth healthy so we don't have to go to the dentist so often, and that's why we brush our teeth."

> **The use of indirect language can be the key to unlocking demand avoidance.**

Below are some other ideas on how you can phrase things indirectly, adding context and reasoning and, where possible, processing time for the Autistic person. This new type of thinking will help you learn to avoid making those direct demands whenever it's practical to do so.

Start by talking more openly about the thing that needs to be done. Maybe there is a clear reason why it can't be done by you or another person that you can explain to the Autistic person. And then, once the needs and reasons are all laid on the table, you can ask for their input, "Do you have any ideas how we can make this work?" Or, "Let's see if we can come up with a solution to this. Do you have any ideas? How can we workshop this problem to make it happen? Then we can both go back to what we want to be doing."

Another example (good for partners of Autistic people) is when I hear my wife say on her way out the door, "Can you wash the clothes today?" Or, "Hey, I need you to wash the clothes. Can you do that today please?"

My response? Instant pressure, instant brick wall.

There is now a high chance that request won't be actioned. Try this angle instead and see what happens; "You know, I really can't see how to stop all this washing piling up. I mean, there are dirty clothes piling up so fast. I really don't see how we can stay on top of this pile; it's getting me down."

No one's asked me to do anything, but my brain is a solution-focused, logical brain. As an Autistic person, that logical side is bigger than the emotional side, so that brain is going to have an automatic response like this: "Well, don't be overwhelmed, there's only one way to fix this problem—it's pretty simple, I'll make a start to wash those clothes." While my partner is already out the door to work by now, I'm in solution mode: "I might as well put a few loads on. I can help with their problem."

Or what about the age-old "clean your room" or "pick up your toys"? This directive might work occasionally on its own or with an added proviso, "You can't watch TV until you've cleaned your room" or whatever goal they have in mind. All kids have to learn responsibilities like these, absolutely. But for parents of Autistic kids, you soon discover these classic lines really don't work a lot of the time.

There are other ways of going about it though: "Hey, little buddy, let's try and beat the clock packing up these things. I wonder if we can beat it. Time starts now." And even if you don't actually start a clock or a countdown, automatically they can be snapped out of the demand to clean their room and into the game because it's fun to do things at breakneck speed, so they just do it.

On a practical daily level, let's say your little one needs to get dressed for school in the morning. You are probably sorely tempted to say, "I told you to get dressed. Why aren't you dressed? Put your uniform on."

And how has that been working for you so far? Thought so.

My wife and I find that by simply saying something as indirect as, "Hey little buddy, who would you like to help you get ready for school today?" This choice can actually trigger the response you're after—actually getting dressed for school because they get to choose. That's not a demand. They might even use that question as a trigger to just get dressed. My son sometimes replies, "I don't want anyone's help. I'm good." Great! But either way, we're not *making* him do anything. We're just suggesting; there is a deeper layer that he is going to school today but it is totally softened by choice and control in some things, as much as we can give to him.

> **"We're all here to help you mate.**
> **Who would you like to help?"**

This roundabout way of showing the Autistic person there are other perspectives and mindsets to look at challenges is limitless. It can be as smooth and easy as the following example. Let's say there's some sort of plumbing issue at our house. My wife could say, "You better call the plumber tomorrow. Orion, can you please make sure you call the plumber?"

Now, as an adult, yes, I will call them at some point, eventually, I guess, after going through a heck of a lot of anxiety over how to make that phone call (see chapter 7 if you skipped ahead). But by now my wife has figured out how to navigate this in a much more logical, comfortable way for me.

She'll say this type of thing instead, "Maybe we could investigate that problem with our plumber." Open-ended sentence. Now of course, logical black-and-white me is all for that, "Yeah, we should definitely contact a plumber and I could just kind of talk it through, explain the problem and see if it's something he can help us with, right?" It doesn't even sound like a demand.

**Get around the anxiety and panic and go indirect.**

### TIP #6:

Another parenting example my wife and I use with our Autistic son is a combination of placement, timing and suggestion. Many times, he'll get home from school and his drink bottle doesn't look like it's been opened all day; the guy's a camel. We could say, "You haven't drunk all day, buddy. Drink. You must drink." Do-do-do-do-do! And perhaps we would if he replied, "Oh yeah, you're right, sorry. I didn't drink all day at school, but now you've told me to, let me just do that right now for you."

No, wishful thinking. Instead, one of us will get a drink bottle—not the school one, a different one—fill it up with water, idle over to where he is and place it gently somewhere nearby within reach and simply say, "Hey, little buddy. Here's your drink bottle if you need it." And then we walk away.

I haven't said, "You must drink this water." I haven't said, "Have a drink. Here's a drink." I've simply said, "Hey buddy, here's a drink bottle if you need it." It looks fresh and different and he might glance at it when I put it down and it might just trigger that physical connection to tell him he is thirsty, a physical sign that his mind has been suppressing all day because of a million other pressing signals and triggers throughout the school day that his brain has to deal with.

## TIP #7:

The next way to beat demand avoidance is all about depersonalising the demands. This is so powerful and so easy to do. The starting point is to try not to personally ask them by name or refer to the actual thing you want them to do as though it's coming from you. This can be done in various ways. For parents of Autistic kids, you can use their favourite toys or even their favourite characters from cartoons, TV or movies.

Our youngest son loves the cartoon *Bluey*. So, we could use the character *Bluey* to ask him to do things or to help him do things. Or we could use his favourite fire truck. Observe.

"What's that, Fire Truck?"

"Oh, Fire Truck says that firefighters love to share their toys with others."

Might not work the first time, might not work every time but it pays to keep this ace up your sleeve. And it's better than saying, "Listen, share your toys!" In fact, I think Fire Truck has more credibility and authority in our house than me. Actually, I don't think, I know. ——→ I cry myself to sleep.

You might think, *Oh, this just sounds like too much effort.* Or, *It's embarrassing. You want me to role play? I hate role-playing.* But hey, I'm an Autistic guy so I get it, I hate role-playing too. If you're a neurotypical parent though, I'm just saying if you can find a way to get past that and concentrate on the end result, utilising role-playing through characters and toys can absolutely work to beat demand avoidance with the Autistic kids in your life.

For Autistic adults, depersonalising comes through more in the indirect language tip, so not using, "Orion, wash the clothes today," but posing a problem that I can help with instead of using the names and the specific demand.

### # TIP 8:

Another hack to beat demand avoidance is to provide choices. Again, it's important to note that anxiety and control go hand in hand. Providing the Autistic person in your life with some sense of control through choices not only puts anxiety at ease, but also allows them to achieve things in situations or events that they might not have achieved if it was just a straight-out demand.

To be clear, I'm not talking about choices in terms of "want to do" or "not want to do." When something needs to get done or needs to happen, you can't go around casually asking your Autistic child, "Would you like to do this or not?" and hoping for the right answer.

This tip is for when something important is on the radar and you give them what control you can. The really practical example is when it's time to get ready for school we might provide our son a choice between two pairs of shoes, "Which shoes would you like to put on for school?" Now, we know he's going to pick one and put them on, whereas if we had just presented him with one pair of shoes, it's like demanding, "Put on your shoes."

The same applies to giving them a choice of appropriate clothing, "What would you like to wear today, little buddy? Shorts or pants?" You get the idea. To help them even further along, it's really useful to have their whole kit laid out as well. Bring the school uniform out and put it on the couch or a good spot where they can see it (but isn't in the way) so it becomes a silent signal to them about what's coming up soon for the day.

Control and choices are just as important for Autistic adults. Here's a tip for partners of Autistic people: my wife might point out there are some loads of washing that need doing, *and* that we need some things from the shops. So, she will open with, "Do you want to do some washing, or would you like to go to the shops today?"

I get a choice of which one I'd rather do, and the answer can change. Some days I want to go outside, some days I don't but both of those tasks must happen today. We need the milk and bread; we need the clothes washed. But the control and the choice of which one I'm going to do, or how it's going to play out, is in my hands.

TIP #9:

My second-last tip on how you can beat demand avoidance is to use an extremely helpful Jedi mind trick. To be crystal clear, my intention with this tip is not to exploit or manipulate Autistic people. It should not be viewed or used as a trick even though that's what I've called it for this purpose. It's just a fun way of engaging with you and broadening your understanding. I'm Autistic, my son is Autistic. My one and only intention is to provide tips that I know can help empower the Autistic person in your life to overcome daily challenges and improve their quality of life.

So, what is the Jedi mind trick?

**Simply ask the Autistic person in your life if they can help you.**

Try reaching out for help with (well-timed) phrases and questions such as, "I've forgotten how to do this. I can't seem to work out how to do this, do you know? I can't seem to do this on my own, could you help me?" These words can really penetrate into an Autistic mind if they see a problem they can help with.

Autistic people in general (and especially from my own experience and certainly my son's) can also have this innate want to help people, to provide some sort of value or use. Any opportunity to help someone which makes us feel needed or valuable is welcomed and we actually really like to do it.

**TIP #10:**

My final tip is to cultivate more compassion, respect and understanding on both ends. If you're Autistic, you have a medically diagnosed disability. It doesn't matter if some people choose not to view it like that. That's cool. But it's just factual. It is what it is. There's good and there's bad. And everyone needs to respect this, embrace this and accept this. You may think there's no need to say this. I can tell you there is.

An Autistic person can't dial back the autism, turn it on or off, or pick and choose when it manifests. And that's no different to anyone with any form of disability or any manifestation of a disability through varying co-occurring conditions or different characteristics. They are there or they are not there. It's so important just to understand this.

Respect that demand avoidance is a manifestation of disability and not something that is somehow willed or created. This assumption is unhelpful on every level. Let's embrace the idea that people have manifestations in different ways, for different reasons. That's what makes people who we are. Whether it's a diagnosable form of PDA or a strong sense that you experience some sort of demand avoidance as an Autistic person. It's okay; learn about yourself, how it works, and put these tips and strategies into practice!

## 📢 BONE TO PICK WITH YOU

Can we please talk about the phrase "I've got a bone to pick with you"?

How big is the bone? Seriously, make up your mind, do you have a problem with me or do you need my help? What are you proposing here? I don't understand. And who picks bones by the way?

# WORKPLACE CHALLENGES

# CHAPTER 14

## WHY AUTISM AND MAINSTREAM WORKPLACES DON'T MIX

I could dedicate a whole book to the challenges Autistic people and other neurodivergent people face trying to work in mainstream workplaces designed for neurotypical employees (and one day I will!).

According to the 2022 Senate Select Committee on Autism, "…the unemployment rate for autistic people (in Australia) is almost eight times that of people without disability." Eight times! This is so much more than a stark statistic sitting on a page in a sterile report. While shocking, it can only hint at the scale and complexities of the issue and the depth of the crusade I am on to educate the pre-enlightened in this campaign.

Addressing the employment issue for neurodivergent people is crucial and long overdue. The positive effects of employment for Autistic people and their families become exponential; a job to go to each day can provide a greater sense of purpose and value to the Autistic person, improve their quality of life now and in the future and enable more opportunities for success, as well as strengthening connections with colleagues, family, friends and community who can support them in their life.

Basically, it feels good to feel a part of something worthwhile. But at its core it's a sense of acceptance we often crave from the neurotypical world. We never receive it, but I'm working on that.

## THE WORLD NEEDS DIVERSITY

First, I need to lay the groundwork for the essential facts that will make you rethink entrenched workplace expectations either as an Autistic employee or a neurotypical employer. Don't be deterred while I rant a little about the fairly obvious ways in which workplaces totally disregard the workplace requirements of their Autistic employees. There exists not only an inability to understand, acknowledge and accept an Autistic person's differences and provide an environment they can thrive in, but also a resistance to understand the benefits of inclusion and neurodiversity from a business perspective.

I want to highlight the totally untapped resource for employers in encouraging neurodiversity in their workforce.

**Neurodiversity is amazing!**

Diversity is a proven and recommended way to invest your money because as you may have been told at some point, don't put all your eggs in one basket. Diversity is also crucial in agriculture and farming. Diversity of partners is also critical in the continued evolution of human beings, and all living creatures for that matter.

So, neurodiversity in the workplace shouldn't be a hard sell. But it is. My brain is Autistic, I can't change it. Most people take a quick glance at neurodivergent people and only see their challenges, but look more closely and you'll see that we have many strengths, especially in a workplace!

I can do things that neurotypical people can do. In fact, I can do certain tasks better than neurotypical people. Throw in the increased productivity that results from many Autistic people's preference to not take breaks in the standard way (we get things done in half the time) and everyone benefits from the satisfaction we get from working hard without distractions until the job is done. ⟶ *Then I crash on the couch and watch TV for hours.*

Employers in a general sense are looking for the best people for the best roles. You can fill those roles with all the same neurotype, or you can add diversity of brains. Autistic brains think differently. We have a completely different operating system to a neurotypical brain. Autistic brains can be many things:

→ Sharp as a tack.

→ Astute.

→ Discerning.

→ Vigilant.

➙ Conscientious.

➙ Honest.

➙ Industrious.

➙ Precise.

➙ Unbiased.

➙ Dependable.

➙ Factual.

➙ Empirical... I could go on.

But seriously, what employer wouldn't want these skills in their team? When you add neurodiversity (different brains) into your team, workplace, corporation and culture, what you get is growth. Not just healthy growth but new growth, niche growth which can give you the edge over competitors and into service realms you would never have dreamed of before. The world is changing and the winners will be progressive thinkers, organisations that embrace new growth and opportunities and neurodiversity to fill unique services with a comprehensive skillset in their team. So, it's not just about me wanting to make the world a better place for Autistic people; the whole approach has exponential benefits for organisations, workplaces, and teams in every industry.

The first step is about spreading greater knowledge and appreciation of the current challenges we face in the workplace through every platform I can get my hands on. And secondly, the practical improvements I promote are not rocket science, nor are they far-fetched, impossible dreams.

> I want to show that by fully applying the principle of HR or Human Resources in workplaces (not just providing ergonomic chairs and a Christmas party) employers can provide Autistic-friendly workplaces with relatively small changes.

In my experience, Human Resources really only extends to accommodating the needs of the neurotypical employees and the making of practical allowances and access for some of the visible disabilities out there. Providing ramps for an employee who uses a wheelchair is an example. However, because neurodivergent people are, generally speaking, able-bodied, we are somehow "not disabled." To the outside world we have an invisible or hidden disability.

A phrase that I coined a few years ago, "mind ramps," seeks to break down this barrier. Physical ramps are required and necessary workplace adjustments for certain employees and are very rarely points of contention. Yet speaking as a person with a neurological developmental disability (condition), where are my "ramps"? I require "mind ramps" to enable me to perform in my daily duties, yet these are nothing more than a strange theoretical idea put forward by an Autistic guy (me) with no HR experience. Though I did drop out of law school, so that should automatically qualify me for a career in HR.

To actually embody the principle of Human Resources means providing an Autistic employee an environment that supports them with the right structure for them to thrive. By that I am referring to many aspects that often go unnoticed to the neurotypical brain to do with the finer details of a physical work environment: the sensations that emanate from those surroundings moment-to-moment throughout the day, the expectations on interactions, the unplanned meetings and events, and many other sudden changes and sensations that can disorientate a divergent brain.

**Put simply, where are the "mind ramps"?**

I've got personal workplace experiences and stories as an Autistic person, from instances that got me fired to suffering months of mental anguish, simply for the bad reputation and assumptions about me by colleagues for nothing more than being Autistic. Let's look at some reasons why this continues to happen and how we can address it. You'll be familiar with these concepts by now but put them in action in a neurotypical workplace and it's like landing in a foreign country not speaking the language.

## UNDERSTANDING MELTDOWNS IN WORKPLACES (AND HOW TO HELP)

So, at a practical level what are the challenges of workplaces for Autistic people? I'm starting straight up with the elephant in the room because in my experience, the biggest challenge to successful long-term employment has been the repercussions of uncontrollable outbursts and meltdowns that have ruined my career.

Key word again being uncontrollable. Why would I intentionally jeopardise my career? Think about it, I love my core passions of radio broadcasting, podcasts, and content creation; they're my strength. I would do them until I die—for free. So, why would I ever want to burn my bridges in a workplace where I was doing my passion and getting paid for it? Why would I want to ruin a career in the one thing I'm passionate about? It's utterly ridiculous. It's unthinkable to me.

And yet the potential for meltdown in the workplace is always there for an Autistic person. I never want to have a meltdown; it is far from enjoyable and can 100% ruin relationships, reputations and careers. The problem is they are an uncontrollable response by your brain and you cannot stop them or grow out of them. It's not like I can take care of them before I leave the house, "Well, I'm leaving home now so I'll put my 'meltdown' cap on the back of the door there. No more meltdowns for me till I get home."

You go to work and it's the real world. My Autistic brain doesn't change whether I'm at home, with family or friends, at school or university, or in the workplace; it does not matter. In fact, meltdowns can be more easily triggered when you're not in what you consider to be a safe space (home in my case).

If you're not Autistic and you see an Autistic person having a meltdown, please don't treat them badly. Don't ostracise them. Don't think, *Whoa, that's a bit aggressive or angry for me.* Or, *Oh, that makes me feel uncomfortable, you can't work here anymore.*

Autistic people constantly feel uncomfortable living and working in a neurotypical world trying to follow a predetermined plan that everyone seems to know, except us. When an Autistic brain passes its capacity or threshold, it triggers certain emotional and physical responses (see my chapter on meltdowns for more explanation) that a neurotypical brain doesn't experience in the same way.

As an Autistic person it's hard for me to identify and process emotions, let alone manage, control or convey them. I often don't really know when I'm being angry. I can have an expressive outburst and you might respond, "Don't be so angry." when in fact, I might not have realised I sounded angry. Instead, I'm thinking I was just getting my point across and being normal, and there was nothing extraordinary in the words or tone I was using. I don't realise how I look or sound to other people; I don't see what's happening in the same way.

> **My wife has helped me understand that what I experience as passion in my communication can be viewed by others (including her) as anger and aggression, even though that is not what I'm experiencing nor is it my intention.**

I understand that in a workplace, angry outbursts are not helpful, ideal, or particularly appropriate. For non-Autistic people, emotional outbursts can seem confronting and inappropriate, but for Autistic people, meltdowns are a manifestation of too many neurotypical pressures that have stemmed from all those things we have mentioned previously: social situations and interactions, sensory discomfort or anxiety from work, or external situations beforehand. Everything has reached the point of overload and sometimes (not that often) this happens in a workplace. You can't ever know what a person is going through without first searching for an understanding and appreciation of their circumstances.

I spent most of my career in radio and media bumbling along undiagnosed. I remember countless work interactions that were just exercises in poor communication. For example, if I was in a meeting talking about a certain project that I had responsibility for, and someone from another area had done things related to my project that I didn't agree with or they hadn't run things past me or my team, my reaction was fairly momentous, "Why on earth would you ever do such a thing without running it by me!" or I might have just stated, "That's just completely wrong!" In my mind these deviations are clearly outrageous.

My reactions were always taken with bad grace but again, it's my Autistic brain thinking in black-and-white terms. The benefit of a diagnosis may have helped, but it still comes down to how much understanding and acceptance of differences that employees and employers are willing to take on.

**If you see an Autistic person experiencing a meltdown or sensory-triggered outburst, the best thing to do is simply allow that person to safely regulate themselves.** They will be past the point of listening, regulation or control (as I was in those situations). Try and observe what may have been happening leading up to the outburst and learn to see the warning signs. It could have related to things you wouldn't suspect to do with sudden changes; having to move desks, a change in their role or hours, a new task, a loud song at someone's desk, whatever it is, these are things that for an Autistic person can be drastic and lead to meltdowns.

You can't "fix" the moment; you can't magically say things that will make them think differently in that moment. It's a release of a lot of built-up stress and anxiety from holding themselves together up to that point and they can't control how it is released. Who knows how many triggers they have already suppressed that day, even getting to work or navigating their home life?

Support them to a comfortable place with supportive words, and when you think it's appropriate, you could ask them what they need. A drink of water? A walk outside? A quiet room? Some time alone? Gently discourage others from antagonising or judging the moment. Employers and fellow colleagues can make a big difference simply by explaining to others what is going on: "They're Autistic and just need time to regulate themselves again, let's give them some space."

But, and it's a big but, this would only be possible if you had already disclosed to your employer that you are Autistic or neurodivergent. That clearly wasn't an option for me pre-diagnosis, but is certainly a dilemma once diagnosed.

**Disclosure of your diagnosis in any part of your life is a deeply personal decision ladened with mines, and often impossible lose/lose dilemmas.**

- Do you diagnose in your job application?
- Do you wait until you've received a job interview?
- Do you hold out until you've secured the role?
- Or, do you not disclose the diagnosis at all to avoid discrimination and the real risk of losing your job?

I cannot answer those questions for you. I want to believe that employers are open and accepting to the workplace needs and adjustments of Autistic people. But deep down I know that is simply not the case.

If ten people apply for a job, nine being neurotypical and one being Autistic, who do you think has the best chance of getting hired? Further, if the workplace adjustments of one Autistic employee are simply "too hard" for an employer, do you really think they will be giving another neurodivergent applicant a chance? Let me save you the suspense. NO! They won't.

# UNDERSTANDING AUTISTIC TRAITS IN THE WORKPLACE

Some of the more hidden challenges for Autistic people shouldn't surprise you by now. But I have a feeling they will, so let's talk about that.

## SOCIAL SKILLS

Clearly, if you experience significant challenges with social skills and your way of interacting and communicating in the workplace is different, this is going to have an effect on you in the workplace because there are so many social expectations that come with navigating office politics. Employers don't tend to ask where you stand with brutal honesty in the workplace when you're sitting in the job interview. They don't ask you how good you are at small talk, reading body language, verbal and non-verbal cues, and all the other things that are assumed in most workplaces.

But all these things are expected from HR after you get the job. Lack of social skills, or a different way of interacting and communicating should not ruin careers. It shouldn't mean that you could be fired over it or given warnings from HR when they come down from their ivory towers and tell the Autistic person, "You better be normal mate, you better stop being Autistic. We can't have any different people making the rest of us feel uncomfortable in this workplace."

A good example of social expectations in a workplace is things like morning tea in the boardroom once a week or staying back for Friday drinks. A neurotypical person might think, *Great, I don't have to work for a while and potentially I'll get free food and drinks, bring it on!*

For me that couldn't be further from the truth. I can either go to these things and alienate myself from the team and HR, or not go to these things and keep working! These social gatherings are getting in the way of me doing my work, work that I love which helps the company to be successful. I don't want to be interrupted by things that get in the way of me doing what I love; they become quite frustrating and stressful. It doesn't make sense to resent this trait because it makes business sense as well.

**As an Autistic person I just want to do my work and everything else is a roadblock.**

But there I am, at a social gathering, coming across in these workplace situations as rude or disinterested or arrogant or just quiet and people take this at face value without knowing any difference. I just have a different brain which often struggles to understand the social interactions and politics of workplaces. Then HR start to throw some labels around and the rest is history. You can't fix reputations in the end, can you? It's close to impossible to remove a label once it's attached, but I'll still die trying.

I can work in teams. I can work with people. But nowadays that's on the premise that people understand I'm Autistic and I think differently. I'm honest, I'm open, I'm raw. I'm different. As long as everything that I do is misinterpreted and taken the wrong way, social interactions at workplaces actually make it harder for Autistic people. You can't dump an Autistic person into a mainstream workplace and simply say, "Good luck." It doesn't work, it's not how it's supposed to be and unfortunately, it's still how it is.

But that's where I come in.

## EXECUTIVE FUNCTION AND FOCUS

Something that you might take for granted that an Autistic person can really struggle with is executive function. When you ask me a question (workplace or not), you need to understand that I need processing time before I answer your question. Remember I also need to process (check) my answer, because if I respond naturally (logically) it might not go down well with you or with the neurotypical world. So, I'm processing the question which can take time and I'm processing the answer. Imagine as an Autistic person, if you're put under stress already, and trying to interact and process everything, general tasks can take longer and our executive function can suffer.

This impediment can then affect our focus. Everyone has trouble staying focused sometimes, but it's a different level for someone like me. As an Autistic person, staying focused on smaller tasks (even if they are important to the bigger goal) can be challenging, especially if I am having to process what's going on in my workplace area or a specific interaction. I hate getting distracted away from my goal, so my focus can be really affected if what I want to achieve is being overshadowed by other tasks. It can look like I'm constantly jumping around or a lack of attention but often it's a consequence of an Autistic brain operating in a neurotypical workplace. There are so many things I want to achieve that I can't keep up with the ideas and make a coherent plan with so many distractions.

## UNWILLING DETACHMENT

Another really helpful aspect to make people more aware of is the disconnection felt by many Autistic people is actually due to unwilling detachment. Personally, I have little to no friends or circle of support. I mean, I have my beautiful wife and my kids that are my blessing in life, but I'm not like a regular neurotypical person who draws on different circles, either of friends, family, community groups, workplaces, sports teams; whatever "group" you can think of, I'm not in it, and that's not necessarily because I don't want to be. It's because of an unwilling detachment built up over time.

Observe. If I have challenges with social interactions, making friends, understanding friends, and these "friendships" keep ending, of course, these experiences are going to affect me. As a defence mechanism I'm going to become detached. If I'm constantly stuck in a vortex of detachment, and can't make connections or attachments, then what am I going to do?

Eventually, I'm going to stay away from even *trying* to make attachments. I'm going to do solitary things like filming videos and podcasts in my room.

> **If you're very bad at something—if you have horrible experiences, can't find people, can't keep friends, people don't like you, they don't understand you— why would you bother continuing to try?**

So, an unwilling detachment can have a massive impact, not just on your personal life, but also your experiences in the workplace. I've worked all over Australia in many workplaces, including working in media with big teams and big organisations at the highest levels. It's not like after working there for significant amounts of time, I didn't want to maintain connections from those experiences. I wanted to leave with as many friends that I had when I went in. As in, none.

No, wait, of course, I wanted to make friends out of those workmates; working in the same industry, we must have had so much in common! I wanted to have long-term, lifelong friendships with people working in the industry I love. Of course I did, who wouldn't? But you have to understand, for a neurotypical person, that idea makes sense when social connections are formed at work and it can be a fun, social situation. But for me, work isn't a social situation. I don't socialise in my social time, let alone my work time! I mean, that's just riddled with anxiety.

So, you can understand how this has been a dominant thread running through my life that I have wondered and agonised over trying to unravel it all. In truth, thinking about it saddens me, genuinely saddens me, and I wish it was not this way.

The people who I've met working in radio—I wish they were still my friends. I wish I could have understood myself better. I value their friendship; I want to be their friend even though I'm going to be a bit different as a friend, different to what they expect of a friend. I have lost touch with just about every genuine connection I made working in radio. I assume they just don't see the value in me as a friend. I am a bother, an annoyance, a bad friend.

> **In fact, when I bump into old friends from radio, they treat me like a stranger. It hurts.**

Not being able to maintain friends or even make friends in the first place in workplaces means you come across like a loner, like an outcast, like a misfit. Every workplace I've ever worked at, even though I just loved working there, there was never a moment where I felt like, *This is my workplace, I belong here, this is where I'm going to be for as long as I can imagine in the future.* I've never felt attached to it, never felt like part of the team. I was just physically there.

It sounds like I don't want to be there in a workplace but I do. I just have complete detachment; I'm completely unwilling as a result of other challenges. This knowledge can be extremely deflating.

# DISCLOSING YOU'RE AUTISTIC TO AN EMPLOYER

Let's talk about this so-called controversial topic. There are a couple of issues around disclosing that you're Autistic or neurodivergent to an employer and when is the right time to do it.

**Disclosure is a personal choice.** There is no right or wrong answer. So, you might not want to disclose until after you've gained employment, and that makes sense, as you've secured the job and are in a position to ask for workplace adjustments. Some choose to never disclose for many different personal reasons.

However, not disclosing is in essence like working as an undiagnosed or yet-to-be-recognised Autistic person. Now that is my area of expertise. As an undiagnosed Autistic person my experiences involved being labelled as rude, brutal, raw, upfront, intense, not a team player, can't play well with others, or too real and too honest. And in a workplace apparently being honest means I'm rude. I thought honesty was the best policy, however, I get a slap on the wrist from HR at the first sign of being honest because it may offend others. So what's the policy? Can we decide on the policy? Make up your mind.

What I've learnt is that there is value in being open and upfront, but there's also value in taking things with you, and not just dumping it on an employer expecting them to know it all and fix it, despite the fact that it is their responsibility and it is discrimination not to provide you with what you require, as a medically diagnosed disability. Perhaps allow some time to get to know the people and situation more, but it is important to be able to present your workplace with as much information as you are comfortable with that can help them and you create a win/win scenario. I've got the good stuff coming right up.

# PRACTICAL WAYS TO IMPROVE THE WORKPLACE FOR AUTISTIC PEOPLE

By now you're asking, "How can we fix this and what can we do to address it?" I've provided the reasons why autism and mainstream workplaces don't mix but there's no point complaining about a problem without offering some solutions. Neurodiversity is amazing and if you want growth you have to look at employing neurodivergent people. So what can you do as an employer to provide an environment we can thrive in?

## OPEN-PLAN OFFICES

Many modern day offices have moved to open-plan offices or communal working places for employees. These environments can be really overwhelming for an Autistic person. Let me describe what it's like, for effect: it's a concentrated space with a large group of people all making various noises while doing mostly different jobs. There are phone calls, conversations, keyboards typing, radios, clients, air conditioning, fans, heaters, smells. In more specific industries there may be all sorts of extreme noises and other activities to factor in. We are bombarded by all that action and can struggle to process it with an Autistic brain.

To embrace diversity, an employer has to look at it from other points of view. There's no use just saying, "Well, everyone who works in this workplace deserves the same treatment and working conditions". As an Autistic person, this isn't a joke, it's extremely daunting. Sensory overload can lead to meltdowns and shutdowns detrimental to productivity—not a good result for the Autistic person or the business or clients they're working for.

Where possible, providing separate or specific working areas away from the open-plan work scenario is ideal. Designating more quiet areas away from the hustle and bustle of the open office will create an environment conducive to their own personal needs and increase productivity. This is not asking too much. As an employer all you will be doing is living up to your responsibilities with regards to providing facilities and solutions for a person with a disability.

> **The disability might be invisible to you, but it's still a legitimate and diagnosed disability.**

Considering the needs of the whole workplace, including Autistic people, ultimately helps the bottom line of a business, and the mental health and the productivity of the Autistic person. Looking after your workforce is the best way to maintain it and avoid hiring and retraining costs.

## ROTATING DESKS

Another workplace example that is extremely challenging for Autistic people is a thing called "hot-desking," where employees regularly move desks, or move areas within the workplace. I can't see the point of it but I'm assuming from a neurotypical point of view, it's about adding freshness or creativity, or productivity or workflow. This scenario actually has the opposite effect for many Autistic people. If they could be moved at any day, any time, for any reason, from my experience, this is going to cause heightened levels of stress and anxiety.

Many Autistic people in my experience have a deep reliance on rituals and routines. It's certainly critical to my day-to-day life. The impact of constantly switching and moving around the workplace, without really any notice or reason, will affect our ability to be productive. Again, consider a separate space for Autistic employees to work where their desk is theirs permanently. The simple act of assigning an Autistic employee a desk permanently can create such great routine and consistency that productivity can only thrive.

Clearly, all workplaces have different environments and not all are offices. But the same principles as what I'm presenting here can be applied and adapted and workshopped with any parameters through open communication about the needs of both parties. With good Wi-Fi there are lots of options to virtually work from anywhere nowadays.

## LIGHTING AND NOISE

Something that is pretty universal to most workplaces, even outdoors, is lighting and noise. Both lighting and noise can cause regular and constant sensory overload for an Autistic person in any environment, not just work. Fluorescent bulbs, bright LED lights, windows without curtains, random and mixed noises, and multiple noises can all combine to have a detrimental effect on an Autistic person from a sensory point of view.

But obviously I don't expect you, as an employer, company, corporation, or business, to turn off your lights, or have complete silence in your workplace. The solution comes down to being able to control some controllables. For example, they can dim lights, or they could turn the lights off in their area, or use a lamp. If the sun is glaring through the window, let them adjust the curtains and do things that aren't going to affect the entire workplace. These little things can have such a large impact on productivity and the mental health of an Autistic person.

Mainstream workplaces like to prove how modern they are but when you think about all the things they call modern— bright LED lights, open-plan offices, and communal social areas—there's nothing about modern workplaces that makes me feel comfortable. Crucially, it is by no means just the physical, structural adjustments of things in the workplace that desperately need to change with the times.

## INTERACTIONS AND COMMUNICATION

Autistic people by diagnosis have significant challenges with social interaction and communication. We see, experience, and interact with the world differently, and there are some real issues in the workplace with Autistic people being reprimanded, treated badly, bullied and even let go for interacting or communicating differently.

There's an expectation that, "Well, we could hire you as an Autistic person, but you are going to need to mask or try to be neurotypical while you're in the workplace. We can't have you going around being yourself." There's probably a thousand people lining up for that very same job, which is why we are disproportionately underemployed.

Why would employers pick me if they can just pick a neurotypical person? And this is the issue around disclosure. Why would you disclose and potentially lessen your chances of employment? But then when you do disclose and ask for workplace adjustments, the dilemma is, will the employer then say, "Okay, well then if you don't like it, go. There's a thousand neurotypical people that want your job."

There's no meaningful reason why employers would ever need to make an effort for Autistic people. This is the issue that neurodivergent people face on a daily basis. "Sorry mate, we liked you before, but now you're being you, the real you, it's not good."

Now I've had experiences where that has actually cost me jobs through relationships with the people in the workplace. So once things are broken or soured, professional relationships break down, even if it's just because it got to a point where they were not prepared to deal with you, the real Autistic you. This is a massive issue in the workplace for Autistic people.

## WORKPLACE GATHERINGS

We've come full circle back to the topic that gets me fired up. In my experience, and I would assume a similar presumption can be made in many workplaces, workplace gatherings, as a general rule, are mandatory. That is employees must go, must attend, must participate in workplace gatherings, events, and activities. And I absolutely understand that for most neurotypical employees, getting out of work and being able to just hang out with your workmates at a gathering or an event is a pretty attractive proposition.

However, for an Autistic person, it can feel like forced "fun," forced socialising, forced behaviour. As an Autistic person, I go to work because I love my job and I love what I do for work. I don't go to work to do non-work related activities. Certainly not things that I'm not even interested in. I don't want to put myself in a social situation that I know I can't handle or process, let alone feel like I'm forced into that situation.

Forcing Autistic employees into attending workplace gatherings and social interactions is forcing them into situations they are not always able to handle, interpret or process. An example of this situation for a neurotypical employee would be to say to them:

All right Jim, you're boarding a plane to a country you've never been to, you'll have to try to speak a language you've never learnt, with customs and cultures you have no idea about and you're going to live there for six months to do your job. And if you can't do it, you're fired.

Looking back at my entire career, I would say what produced the most anxiety and the most overwhelm were the forced social gatherings. Interacting on a social level with the people I work with every day is hard enough. If you add in clients I've never met before, the idea is really, really scary. It's not about them; it's about me and my abilities to operate in those foreign environments.

Whatever employers may think social gatherings are going to cultivate, I can tell you they are not going to cultivate anything with me. They're probably going to alienate me further, creating more of a gap. Going for drinks at a bar, going to the bowling alley together, Christmas parties—these are all noisy environments, people are talking loudly in your face, conversations really ramp up the interpretation stakes. Being forced into these things in no way helps me with my team, or my productivity.

The pretty simple solution to this problem is giving the option to attend these types of workplace gatherings and encouraging your employees to feel comfortable to say, "It's not my thing, I don't operate at my best under those conditions."

The reason employers offer these social gatherings is so the team works better, and lifts productivity and morale, so why would anyone force people into these situations when for them, it's only going to lower their morale and lower their productivity? It's a no brainer.

## SURPRISE MEETINGS

The predictability of meetings is important to me. Having plenty of advance notice of meetings and team catch-ups is crucial so I can plan for them and manage the related stress in the best possible way. I know in some instances, last minute meetings are just part and parcel of business. They just have to happen as a result of something unexpected and I understand that.

But it's important to accommodate your employees as much as possible because the effects of a surprise meeting on an Autistic employee can skyrocket their anxiety. If a surprise meeting or an impromptu team catch up is suddenly on the agenda for the day, try to give an Autistic employee the most notice. Let them know first, and give them a solid timeframe, a solid reason and as much context as possible so they can process and prepare. If you want to meet "in five," could it possibly wait an hour, so all the staff have time to prepare for the topic?

If it means the Autistic employee has to stop a task they're doing, that will potentially have consequences for their focus for the whole day. I go in with a clear plan for my day and that doesn't incorporate things that are unannounced; my brain just doesn't work that way. I am so productive when I make a plan and can stick to it.

When this isn't possible, all I'm saying is think quickly and communicate as soon as possible with the most notice that is viable to the situation. If you can, discuss with the Autistic person how it affects the tasks they were already working on, and add in some flexibility for them where it works for both sides.

## DRESS CODE

The final and possibly surprising point about the challenges of the mainstream workplace is around dress code. Strict dress codes in workplaces can have a detrimental impact on an Autistic person in many ways. I need to wear things that I'm comfortable in, which does limit my professional choices.

I really like to wear colourful or bright clothing and textures that I find easy and comfortable. So all these things again limit my choices. Clothing and sensory overload really go hand in hand. I tell you, as an Autistic dad with an Autistic child, it can be a daily occurrence to have to cut off a tag or something uncomfortable connected to a piece of clothing; between the two of us, it happens all the time. There are very few tags on any of our clothing anymore, which doesn't help when trying to work out sizes, and if things get lost. However, the feel of clothing is so important. For an Autistic person, you can be hypersensitive to a lot of types of materials; they just don't feel right and get under your skin. This feeling can actually stop you in your tracks. You can't function.

So wearing the right clothing is critical. Suits and certain office wear can be really claustrophobic, restrictive, or feel too rough or even too smooth on your skin, as though you're being touched. Leather shoes and work shoes can be really tight around your toes and your feet. I know that sounds ridiculous but we're talking about heightened sensitivity here, like someone is squeezing your feet. It's distracting and unsettling. So from my point of view, I tend to wear sneakers or casual shoes with the laces undone or at least loosened. It doesn't look great, but it keeps me comfortable and certainly averts any sensory overloads or meltdowns, which is good for everyone.

Clearly I have my own unique style, like most Autistic people I know. But I hope that you understand we're not just trying to be different or look different or declare, "We don't accept your silly fashions." No, number one, it's about our personality. But number two, and most importantly, it's about our needs from a sensory point of view. This is just something to keep in mind if you're about to introduce a uniform or strict dress code in your workplace; try to maintain flexibility and open-mindedness about your reasons, and consider time, place and purpose.

## PROFESSIONALISM

I've been looking forward to talking (ranting) about professionalism. "Why?" you may ask. Well, in my view professionalism or acting in a professional manner is a fallacy. It's a made-up term, without any real meaning. As an Autistic person, the use of the term professionalism or acting in a professional manner is completely unhelpful. Rather than hijacking random values and conflating them into a cesspit called professionalism, why not just use actual values in the workplace?

And no, I am not talking about those made up corporate "core values" or mission statements. Imagine if HR, who are for the most part completely irrelevant anyway, ceased using the term professionalism (acting in a professional manner) and replaced it with tangible values specific to that workplace.

So, you are hired and fired based on the specific values of your team and workplace. Values, unlike made up terms like professionalism, are concrete, black-and-white, specific ways of viewing things that Autistic people require. And more broadly, they actually make sense to all employees. If you have a value of honesty or integrity, I can measure that. I might not measure it the same as you, but I can measure it.

The next point to make is that in general terms, an employer's HR policy on working in a professional manner is based on a neurotypical brain, with no apparent view taken on other neurodivergent minds. I can't ever meet the neurotypical standard of professionalism. A neurodivergent brain cannot meet the expectations of a neurotypical brain. It's impossible.

So the idea of professionalism is not only discriminatory to any employee who is not neurotypical, it's also fanciful. The overarching point with regards to reasonable adjustments, under the professionalism banner, is flexibility and understanding. In essence, professionalism says, "There is only one way for all people in this workplace to act. You must act in a professional manner." But if you have neurodivergent employees, they have completely different operating systems. If professionalism says there is only one way you can act regardless of the brain you have, regardless of the disability you may or may not have, who is being unprofessional, me or HR?

> In my view, the most effective and reasonable workplace adjustments are to people, not things. Adjusting the attitudes and level of understanding of one employee to another beats dimmable lights any day of the week.

## EDUCATION

Another inclusive practice that employers can implement today is staff education. Encourage your employer to empower their staff with the education and knowledge of their fellow employees who are neurodivergent. Sure, you could make your employees do another one of those online tick-a-box tests every twelve months, but no employee in the history of the world has ever learnt anything from those stupid online HR tests.

I think it's critical that employers utilise the expertise and lived experiences of neurodivergent advocates who can speak to your staff in a way that will engage, connect, enlighten, and educate them.

My hope is that these challenges and solutions I have outlined in this chapter have provided some insights and understanding around aspects of the workplace that can seem harmless to neurotypical workers but can actually have genuine, serious and detrimental impacts on Autistic employees. You can see now that adopting slight changes and being slightly more flexible can not only help Autistic people, but also helps productivity and your bottom line.

There is a vast, untapped resource for all corners of business and industry that have not yet seen the potential of the Autistic employee! The fact my Autistic son may one day benefit from the opportunity this awakening will bring keeps me striving (uphill) everyday.

## 📣 NOT BAD

Do you ever ask someone, "How are you?" and they reply with, with, "Not bad"?

Not bad?! I didn't ask, "How aren't you?" I asked, "How are you?" "Well, I'm not bad, I can tell you that much." Okay, but you haven't answered the question. Should we go through the list of emotions and tick off the ones you aren't until we finally identify what you are? And everyone lies anyway, someone could tell you they're, "Pretty good actually, pretty good", and two minutes later you spot them in the corner crying because they are in fact NOT good.

I'll tell you what they're not good at, they're not good at answering questions, that's for sure.

# FAREWELL | **WHE**RE **TO** **FR**OM **HE**RE?

My friend, you've made it this far so I'm guessing you're with me for the long haul. Which is half the battle, so thank you. You've shown me you are committed to change, gaining greater understanding, showing empathy and kindness to others' differences, and a need to know more and question the misconceptions and assumptions that have relegated Autistic people to a subcategory of humans for too many generations.

How can we measure the ways Autistic people have been held back, judged, derided and discriminated against? How do you measure the impact of social misunderstanding, broken dreams and severed relationships scattered behind us?

We truly can't. While the Australian government has made an attempt to quantify elements, I honestly can't help but wonder if, in ten years' time, **the results of The Senate Select**

**Committee on Autism report will still be barren, futile words on a page very few change-makers have read, let alone acted on?**

I fear so. History says so.

Upon first reading the prognosis of the report, I felt astounded, broken, heartbroken, angry, frustrated. I felt like busting down Parliament's door. I felt a profound agitation that has haunted me every day since. I didn't want to read about what I already knew. My son can't wait for someone else's solution or wait for words like strategy, action plan and roadmap to have some sort of actual meaning in his life.

He can't rely solely on neurotypical people to formulate solutions for Autistic people. Surely it's a collective effort to forge new understanding and implement supportive environments. I thought about what I could do in response to the report. What would be my "action plan"? What was my activism? *Stuff it!* I thought. *I can start right now by creating content.* I grabbed my phone and I was rolling. I recorded a podcast and video at the same time, getting on both platforms straight away. Sometimes you have to rant to break the cycle, you have to scratch the record like I'm doing to people.

In my experience, there are so many adults who have gone undiagnosed or misdiagnosed for decade after exhausting decade (and there are those still battling life undiagnosed).

> It's an epidemic; there's a lost generation of Autistic kids who are now adults like myself, coming to a realisation that much of what has plagued their life has not been autism at all, but rather the society, the civilisation, the culture, even the family they have been born into.

Acceptance is quite possibly the single hardest thing to achieve for an Autistic person, including acceptance from their own family and friends. Forget the broader society, schools and workplaces; it can be close family and friends that never whole-heartedly accept an Autistic person for who they intrinsically are. But you can change that.

In a perfect world, if you had a child who was born Autistic, you would accept they are Autistic. You would accept they were born Autistic and they will die Autistic. They will live their entire life as an Autistic person. That's my idea of a perfect world, that level of acceptance. It seems really simple, but it's not achievable for many.

Perhaps I have an advantage in that I am Autistic and therefore it is easier for me to fully accept my Autistic son for his true self and understand his true nature. This doesn't mean it doesn't drive me nuts sometimes. Raising an Autistic child is one of the greatest challenges and achievements you will experience. → Hang on—there's a bloody chapter on parenting, read that.

My personal price of understanding this situation is suppressing some of my Autistic self in order to be a fully present, engaged, supportive father for all the practical time I can produce within myself for him and his brother. I can pay this price because I understand it beforehand and can prepare for it in the right environments that my partner and I have created together.

While research into neurodivergence continues (painstakingly slowly), there persists an archaic nature of intolerance and misunderstanding amongst the wider society. Mankind seems determined to prove that we will denounce everything we don't understand. The reality is, many people will only see signs of autism when it has reached boiling point; they will witness meltdowns, shutdowns and burnouts and form opinions of Autistic people solely by these encounters, based on these behaviours without any context at all.

These assumptions, while nothing more than misguided conjecture and speculation, are wildly powerful notions that only produce further misunderstandings. Nowadays, I try to practice compassion and openness over judgement, rather than assuming something about someone. If law school taught me anything, it is that you must learn to temper your natural (potentially biased) judgments and conclusions with a full understanding and appreciation of all sides involved.

I don't want people to think I'm more Autistic or less Autistic than others, I'm just different. I've got individual strengths and challenges, no different to anyone else. It's important to remember that everyone has different needs and they can be fluid. I might have low care needs compared to others, but they are fluid; some days I can barely function. And likewise, don't write off someone who is classed as having high care needs as having nothing to offer. They will 100% have incredible strengths that we can all benefit from, if we take the time and care to listen and communicate in flexible ways. We can explore the universe for goodness' sake, so learning to communicate in a multitude of ways is not asking too much, and like learning a second language, should be part of every curriculum.

## 📢 CLOTHES OFF THEIR BACK

"She's so nice, she would give you the clothes off her back." How many layers of clothing does this person wear? And if she's so nice, wouldn't she give away clothing from her closet, rather than her person? What about the bottom half, who doesn't need pants?

## KEY TAKEAWAYS

Let's highlight the key takeaways to remember when you close this book and lend it to everyone you know. Wait, that's a horrible idea and who in the history of the world has ever returned a book they borrowed off a friend? Anyway, let's highlight the key takeaways to remember when you close this book and buy more copies as gifts for everyone you know so you can keep this copy.

If you care for an Autistic person, firstly let's acknowledge **how amazing you are for being their supporter,** someone they can rely on. They trust you to keep them safe and to allow them to be themselves when they're ready, supporting their needs. This position of love and trust can't be underestimated. It can grow and change but an Autistic person doesn't outgrow needing and relying on you. Initially this position is filled by parents or caregivers and then it might be mates, then it might be partners, spouses and sometimes, if you're lucky, a wonderful boss or colleague.

The Autistic person in your life relies on you. It's a very special relationship that can be the springboard to achieve so much in an Autistic person's life, whatever form that achievement comes in: maintaining a single incredible friendship, gaining meaningful employment, pursuing their passion beyond the home, or perhaps being a voice to the Autistic community (thanks Renee!).

After reading of the reality and reasons behind some Autistic behaviours, I also hope you will **head off into the Autistic world with more compassion.** If you can now view shutdowns and meltdowns as uncontrollable actions, you will view them in a more kind, compassionate manner and leave the judgement, anger, and resentment behind.

Remember how deeply exhausting these responses are for the Autistic person as well. Feeling compassion will help you respond in the most appropriate way, providing that Autistic child or adult some alone time, some quiet time and some time away to get over the meltdown and clear the exhaustion. Compassion will help bring them back to a point where they can re-enter the world that much sooner.

One of the most important tips to help the Autistic person in your life is to **be their advocate—advocate for them.** Be your Autistic child's, partner's, friend's, family member's biggest advocate! Use your strengths as a neurotypical person to help the Autistic person in your life find their passions, their strengths, their special interests, and their place.

For parents of Autistic kids or friends and families of Autistic people, try to help them find training, courses, employment and opportunities that match their special interests. See through the lens of their special interests, their passions, the things that they just live for, the things that feed their mind and nourish their life.

> **Using those passions as a window, as a lens, you can then teach them things they need to be taught in a relatable, engaging, natural way; that's the key.**

A note of caution: advocacy is a double-edged sword in my opinion. Too often, advocacy is neurotypically presented. We've reached the point now (thank you so much for everyone's help) where it's unacceptable for an organisation that is based on serving Autistic people to be *solely* (I use that word because I don't mean to say "fire all the non-Autistic people") run by neurotypical people.

If you want to have a parent of an Autistic child become the CEO of an autism-focused company, that's great. I'm saying you can't solely run a company serving and supporting the needs of Autistic people (receiving government funding to serve the Autistic community) without having Autistic people be an integral part of the company. And this does not mean hiring Autistic people on a casual basis to "consult" or provide "feedback" once a month on the premise that their insights are non-binding and for guidance at best.

**In fact, I strongly feel that organisations taking government funding to provide services for Autistic people should ensure they have Autistic people at all levels of the organisation.**

Non-Autistic parents can have the very best intentions for supporting and advocating for their Autistic child, but sometimes the biggest challenge for Autistic people is the non-Autistic people closest to them. Sometimes, it's not the world we've got to fight, it's fighting to be seen for what we can do. Too often, I see "advocacy" based on infantilising and ableist views. Or advocacy based on their child being "special," based on highlighting their child's disability to a toxic degree like referring to autism as their "superpower."

There's no other group that I receive more criticising comments from than neurotypical parents of Autistic kids. What always staggers me is how a parent of an Autistic child speaks to me, an Autistic person: "How dare you speak on behalf of my Autistic child! It's ridiculous to call yourself the same thing as my non-verbal Autistic child."———▶ *The correct term is non-speaking.*

"Don't put yourself in the same box as people who actually have autism!"

*The preferred language is Autistic, not "has autism."*

**I'm not speaking on their behalf.** I'm speaking on my own behalf, drawing on my experiences as an Autistic person. But understand this: I'm devoting countless hours to creating content that will help increase the community's understanding, acceptance and appreciation of Autistic people, in order to help my Autistic son and every other Autistic person on the planet if I can. They deserve the same rights, privileges and quality of life afforded to everyone else. These parents get pretty high and mighty that I'm not really Autistic and can't possibly understand what they or their Autistic child are going through, but that was never my intention because every Autistic person is different.

Oh, and to be clear, I do not need nor ask for anyone's permission to devote my life to making a positive difference to the lives of my fellow Autistic people. To stir up the critics further, in my experience there are non-Autistic parents out there who have (however unintentionally) basically leveraged their disabled child to make a successful career in content creation and advocacy. But let me ask you this, what did they fix? What have they done? According to the Senate Select Committee on Autism report, nothing.

Their child still has a 20-year life expectancy differential, along with twice the mortality rate of the general population.[13] Take a gasp at the other risks presented in the report's executive summary:

> Autistic people experience high rates of co-occurring mental health conditions and are more likely to attempt or commit suicide than other groups. Seventy-five per cent of autistic people do not complete more than a Year 12 education, while the unemployment rate for

autistic people is almost eight times that of people without disability. Autistic people also appear to be overrepresented in the justice system and at higher risk of homelessness than the general population.

Inclusion of autistic people in the community is also poor, with many experiencing loneliness, isolation, exclusion and discrimination. Significant numbers of autistic people report having no friends other than family or paid staff. Likewise, many families say they feel unwelcome at community events, or unable to leave the house due to negative public reactions to their child's autism.[14]

You can see the action plan needs to change desperately. The way forward needs to include the very people who are being disadvantaged in the formation of the action plan.

All the work my wife and I are doing for our son, talking and working together endlessly with every relevant stakeholder in his life, all the work you see and the work you don't see, will eventually build to the point where his education will be a well-oiled machine, giving our son the best possible opportunity to receive an education like any other child has the right to receive.

**Autistic people are entitled to the same rights and privileges as every other person. That is all I am fighting for.**

Another major part of advocating for Autistic people is understanding that Autistic people can be taken advantage of. They can be exploited. As their advocate you need to look out for those warning signs. For example, if the Autistic person in your life is approached by organisations to provide some sort of insight as an Autistic person, make sure they're paid for their work—just like any neurotypical person would be paid for the same work for their 'insights'.

> Hey, what are we going to pay these Autistic people for spending a day recording a video that we can use to promote ourselves for the next couple of years?

> Well, it's not going to be money that's for sure. We'll give 'em some putty and some fidget spinners, they'll love it, they'll be thanking us!

No. Pay Autistic people for their work!

If you're an organisation that advocates for Autistic people and you use Autistic people to advocate for you and you don't pay them, you are not an advocate of Autistic people. Similarly, it's not uncommon for the younger demographic of Autistic people to not actually have the ability to judge when someone is a friend and can be taken at their word, and when someone is a bully, actually taking advantage of them.

As an Autistic person with an Autistic son, I can look at it on both sides here. As a kid, I can say absolutely that a lot of my childhood experiences with my friends weren't great. I thought they were my friends but I never seemed to get treated very nicely by them. And when you're a kid and you're Autistic, even if it's undiagnosed, you just want to be accepted and feel part of something; you just want friends. It's a lonely, lonely life. So, you tend to put up with a lot of crap, and you don't even see it as bad.

Now as a dad, I can look at my son and see he thinks that a particular person is his friend. But I can tell you from the stories he's telling of the experiences that that kid is not my son's friend. That kid who my son thinks is a close friend is absolutely not a friend. He's stealing all his cards and taking his stuff, and saying stupid things on the bus. It's like my son's a circus animal for him, he's an attraction, and my son is too young to see this. I know what's going on and slowly, my son will too; it will take time for him to learn some of the skills to protect himself. My advice is to look out for that if you have a child who's Autistic; and, they're lucky to have someone looking out to protect them as well.

Finally, to be clear, this book is in no way a diagnostic tool. You should not use this book to diagnose yourself, your child or anyone for that matter. It's simply a discussion by an actual Autistic guy. And if, by reading this book, you resonate with the content and suspect that you could be Autistic, my recommendation is to consult with your local GP or family doctor as a starting point.

Autism is for life. Every Autistic person is different and has their own individual challenges and strengths. **Autism isn't linear, it's a spectrum, like a colour wheel of infinite colours and possibilities.** As long as prejudice and discrimination are the order of the day, the argument whether to disclose a diagnosis has no end to it. You can only do what feels right to you in a particular situation.

Whether you are Autistic or not, don't put pressure on yourself that you are going to learn all these skills and tips I've talked about overnight. I've built them up over a lifetime of learning. The goal in life can only be to build on yourself as a person, show off your strengths, find more tools to improve on your weaknesses and love both sides because that is how you were born, Autistic or otherwise.

No one actually reads this far right? But if that is the case, how will I ever know? No one will read this far to answer my question… you know what, forget it. Why are you reading this far anyway? Grow up!

# 📢 I'M HEARING YOU

In my view, the key components of a conversation are talking and listening. To speak and to be heard. So why is it in some conversations people will respond with "I hear you" or "I'm hearing you"? Is this a sound check to our actual conversation? "Hi mate, how are you? I'm hearing you."

"Yeah, I'm hearing you too."

You're hearing me, are you? Good! That's the whole point of a conversation, "I'm hearing you" is a given. Without hearing someone in a conversation, there is no conversation. Next time we have a conversation, how about you tell me something you really want me to hear, and I'll just respond with "I'm ignoring you."

# **ACKNOWLE**DGEMENTS

O f all the parts of writing a book, the acknowledgements is by far the most confronting. You see, traditionally this is where the author thanks people who have encouraged, motivated and supported them. Presumably they do so to convey appreciation in a permanent and public way. Apparently the dedication page doesn't adequately fulfil that role. And who reads this section anyway? Seriously, get to the good stuff! This book is pure gold!

Further, the author often fills the page with a seemingly endless list of supportive family, friends, colleagues, mentors, and other miscellaneous people involved in their life. As an Autistic person with an Autistic child, my sole reason for creating content like this book is to seek and establish understanding and appreciation for Autistic people. Neither permanent, nor public appreciation is a given for Autistic people, or any person who is deemed different by society in any way.

I have no long list of family, friends, colleagues, mentors and other miscellaneous people in my life. Let alone a long list of supportive people to thank. So, I would like to take this opportunity to thank every single person who at some point in my life plainly rejected, disposed of, or refused to appreciate and accept me. Because of you, this book and every piece of content I have ever produced was created. However, without an audience there is no content and I am forever grateful to each and every member of my YouTube and broader content community. Without you, I am just an Autistic guy ranting into the abyss.

Seriously, to Renee and our sons, Conan and Hugo, can you just skip to the dedication section for your "permanent and public" acknowledgement; there is nothing to see here.

Finally, I wish to convey my genuine and heartfelt thanks and gratitude to the incredible team at Dean Publishing with a special mention to my dream team, Natalie Deane, Suzan Dalziel and Jazmine Morales. Although, to be fair I feel like I taught them more than they taught me.

# ABOUT THE AUTHOR

Alleged

O rion Kelly is proudly Autistic and dedicated to raising your level of understanding, acceptance and appreciation of Autistic people.

Orion lived undiagnosed for decades until after the birth of his first child. His adult diagnosis was a revelation and a turning point, illuminating the beauty of neurological differences that exist within human beings, as well as acknowledging the enormous struggles and challenges of trying to live life in a world designed for neurotypical people.

Today, Orion crusades tirelessly for better awareness, respect and opportunities for his Autistic son than he experienced at school and every neurotypical workplace he battled in. Using his passion for communication and content creation, Orion's perceptive, often provoking insights as an Autistic person cut to the heart of humanity's incapacity for tolerance and accepting differences.

Along with his Autistic advocacy, Orion is a consultant, keynote speaker, author, actor, host, YouTuber, podcaster and radio broadcaster based in Victoria, Australia. Orion hosts the podcast "My Friend Autism" and has his own Autistic-focused YouTube channel. Orion also hosts and produces podcasts for organisations and companies, MCs events and is available as a keynote speaker.

In a commercial radio career spanning over 25 years, Orion has worked ON AIR at 3GG and Star FM (Gippsland), KIIS 1011 / Mix (Melbourne), 92.9 (Perth), 2Day FM (Sydney), B104.9 / Star FM (Albury), 3NE / Edge FM (Wangaratta), 2LF (Young) and 4VL (Charleville).

Orion has also worked as a presenter for Seven (Perth), Fremantle Dockers Football Club (Perth), Southern Cross Ten (Gippsland) and Crown Casino (Melbourne). Orion studied acting at 16th Street Actors Studio (Melbourne) and has featured in short films along with some blink-or-you'll-miss-it parts in various television series.

# **END**OTES

1   Select Committee on Autism, 2022, 'Services, support and life outcomes for autistic Australians', *The Senate report,* Parliament of Australia, viewed 17 November 2022, https://www.aph.gov.au/Parliamentary_Business/ Committees/ Senate/Autism/autism/Report.

2   ibid.

3   Rylaarsdam, L & Guemez-Gamboa, A 2019, 'Genetic causes and modifiers of autism spectrum disorder', *Frontiers in Cellular neuroscience*, vol 13, p 385, viewed 17 November 2022, https://doi. org/10.3389/fncel.2019.00385.

4   American Psychiatric Association 2022, *About DSM-5-TR*, webpage, Washington, DC, viewed 17 November 2022, https://www.psychiatry.org/psychiatrists/practice/ dsm/about-dsm.

5   Dyer, K 2013, 'Applied Behaviour Analysis' in Volkmar, FR (ed), *Encyclopedia of Autism Spectrum Disorders*, Springer, New York, https://doi.org/10.1007/978-1- 4419-1698-3_1004.

6   SSM Health 2022, *Savant syndrome*, webpage, Treffert Centre, Wisconsin, viewed 17 November 2022, https://www.ssmhealth.com/treffert-center/conditions-treatments/savant-syndrome.

7   Jones, SC, Akram, M, Gordon, CS, Murphy, N & Sharkie, F 2021, 'Autism in Australia: Community knowledge and autistic people's experiences', *Journal of Autism and Developmental Disorders*, vol 51, no 10, pp 3677-3689, viewed 17 November 2022, https://www.ncbi.nlm.nih.gov/pmc/articles/PMC7778837.

8   Loomes, R, Hull, L & Mandy, WPL 2017, 'What is the male-to-female ratio in autism spectrum disorder? A systematic review and meta-analysis', *Journal of the American Academy of Child and Adolescent Psychiatry*, vol 56, no 6, pp 466-474, viewed 17 November 2022, https://pubmed.ncbi.nlm.nih.gov/28545751

9   Minio-Paluello, I, Porciello, G, Pascual-Leone, A & Baron-Cohen, S 2020, 'Face individual identity recognition: a potential endophenotype in autism', *Molecular Autism*, vol 11, p 81, https://doi.org/10.1186/s13229-020-00371-0.

10  Katsnelson, A 2021, *Autistic children may have trouble predicting movements*, webpage, Simons Foundation, California, viewed 17 November 2022, https://www.spectrumnews.org/news/autistic-children-may-have-trouble-predicting-movements/.

11  Geggel, L 2014, *Analysis finds high rates of gut problems in autism*, webpage, Simons Foundation, California, viewed 17 November 2022, https://www.spectrumnews.org/news/analysis-finds-high-rates-of-gut-problems-in-

autism/#:~:text=It%20found%20that%20children%20
with,feel%20abdominal%20pain%20 than%20controls.

12 Turner, M 2020, 'The role of drugs in the treatment of autism', *Australian Prescriber*, vol 43, pp 185-190, viewed 17 November 2022, https://www.nps.org.au/australian-prescriber/articles/the-role-of-drugs-in-the-treatment-of-autism.

13 Select Committee on Autism, 2022, 'Services, support and life outcomes for autistic Australians', *The Senate report,* Parliament of Australia, viewed 17 November 2022, https://www.aph.gov.au/Parliamentary_Business/Committees/ Senate/Autism/autism/Report.

14 ibid.